Working with Csongor Daniel and seeing the fantastic results of his biotherapy, I am not surprised by the depth of insight into health and disease that his book provides. I consider <u>Biotherapy, A Healing for the 21st Century</u> a must read for anyone interested in health and healing!

Dr. Todd H. Slaughter A.P.
Doctor of Acupuncture RI
Acupuncture Physician FL
National Board Certified (NCCA)

Daniel's main objective is to show you that you don't have to be gifted in order to become a healer. All you need is desire and knowledge, which you'll definitely find in this book. Within easy to understand directions is hidden a powerful wisdom that anyone can acquire.

Tina Romanowski M.S., A.R.N.P, Certified Specialist

Biotherapy is a new, understandable, yet comprehensive science of energy balancing, fit for everyday use both by professionals and any open minded individual.

Karin Galliano M.A., M.S., L.M.H.C.

BIOTHERAPY

A HEALING FOR THE 21ST CENTURY

BIOTHERAPY

A HEALING FOR THE 21ST CENTURY

THE EASTERN EUROPEAN METHOD OF ENERGY BALANCING THAT ANYONE CAN MASTER

CSONGOR DANIEL
WITH FOREWORD BY
ROBERT J. MIGNONE, M.D.

Printed in the United States of America
Library of Congress Catalog Card Number: 97-92184
ISBN: 0-9658781-0-4
Illustrations: Csongor Daniel and Slavka Zsolnai
Page design: Csongor Daniel
Cover design: Donald C. Donzal and Csongor Daniel
Cover photos: Karen Daniel and Kathryn Wishlow

2733 Lawyer Terrace
North Port, FL 34286
(941) 423-8660

To my mother, my father, my Aunt Margit, and all my friends and family, who would make this list very, very long.

Contents

Foreword

This is more than the story of one young man's discovery of his special gifts for healing. It speaks to all of us about possibilities for cultivating and using energies to heal ourselves and others. It is especially timely as our western culture breaks out of the archaic mind/body split and begins to embrace the wholeness of our humanness.

What for centuries had been one of the mainstays of relieving suffering, healing became intellectually and politically incorrect during this past century's scientific revolution and emphasis on Newtonian understanding of energy and matter. A linear concept of matter has been the focus of our microscopes, radiographs, stethoscopes and other medical technologies. Our culture bought the mind/body split hook line and sinker. As a result, our technological medicine has soared while the heart and soul of it has withered into dire straits.

The emergence of humanitarianism, modern ethics and the shift of collaborative decisionmaking in healthcare are but a few examples of profound changes in our understanding of health and illness. In addition, Einsteinian physics, with its understanding of the interchangability of energy and matter, is an especially exciting and revolutionary conceptualization.

Books like "Vibrational Medicine" by Gerber describe much of the science that has evolved to what contemporary physicists now accept as constructs of the day. We in medicine, on the other hand, seem to still be debating whether the world is round or flat, whether the mind and the body are one. We seem wedded to a myopic view of physical matter that we can measure with our five senses. If we can't do that, then we must visualize or conceptualize some of our phenomena into "stuff".

This book is a readable and practical introduction to the energetic dimensions of biology and health. The author shows through his own example something of the struggle to truly shift the paradigms and have others know about it. His courage and determination, however, kept him on track so as to be able now to enlightens further with his experience. He even includes some practical suggestions for ways that we can further our own capacity to experience and use our energetic self as it interacts with our physical self.

In that sense, this provides another step for humankind on the journey to expanded understanding and influence of health and disease, relief and suffering.

Robert J. Mignone, M.D.

Robert J. Mignone, M.D. has 20 years experience teaching and practicing in the Boston area and at Mass General Hospital, Harvard Medical School. He trained at Duke (M.D.), Yale (Medicine), Cornell (Neurology), and Harvard (Psychiatry). He is Chief of Behavioral Medicine at Charlotte Regional Medical Center in Punta Gorda, FL., and is on staff at Fawcett Memorial and St. Joseph Hospitals in Port Charlotte, FL., and at Sarasota Memorial and Doctor's Hospital in Sarasota, FL. He is also Clinical Professor at School of Nursing at the University of South Florida, founder and CEO of Healthsmart Productions, Inc., and Medical Director of Gulf Coast Health Services, Inc. Doctor Mignone is a founding member of the American Academy of Medical Acupuncture and a lifetime member of the American College of Forensic Psychiatry.

Acknowledgment

Thanks to all my friends and my family who believed in me from the very beginning. This book would have never been written without the unconditional love and support from my parents, Aunt Margit, "Uncle" Joe, and my wife Karen. Special thanks to all my American friends for improving my English, particularly Suzanne Frame, who has done such a beautiful job proofreading my manuscript.

INTRODUCTION TO BIOTHERAPY

The human mind is incapable of comprehending total reality. In fact, there is much more beyond our knowledge than we can ever imagine. The material world and the mysteries of the universe are inexhaustible, and sometimes inaccessible. Consequently, we are in need of some abilities that go beyond the physical world. In this new world, we would have endless opportunities because it would be controlled by our own mind. The mind is the place where we can travel the whole universe without taking one step!

It is commonly known that we use barely ten percent of our brain capacity. So, where is the rest? It is there, but we have never been taught how to use it, and unfortunately, there is small possibility of learning to utilize it in a lifetime. But, there is a chance to extend our mind power and our senses to a certain level where we can enjoy its benefits much more than we do now.

The potential of the human brain is endless. Just think a little bit: How many times have you thought of someone, and at the same moment the phone rang, and that person was on the other end of the line? How many times have you dreamt of something, only for it to actually happen in the future? How many times have you walked on the street, knowing without turning back that someone was behind you? How about when your child is hurt? After a few strokes over the painful spot, or a kiss, the ache is gone. Have you ever felt good or bad, sick or in excellent health, lucky or unfortunate, happy or sad for no obvious reason? Have you ever heard of some unbelievable, miraculous healings?

Have you ever tried to find the answer to all these questions? The answer is easy: A universal life-force called BIOENERGY.

Bioenergy simply means "living energy". Maybe you've heard of it under some different names such as Qi, Chi, Prana, Ki, Aura, Animal Magnetism, Bioplasma, etc. They all mean the same: An electromagnetic field that surrounds and is a part of every living being. It controls our bodies in ways we can hardly imagine. We actually are more energy-beings than only flesh and blood. Quantum physics explains this theory very clearly, however, if you are not familiar with it, I suggest a simple exercise that will remove all doubts from your mind:

Sit or lie down into a comfortable position and close your eyes. Take a few deep breaths and relax. You are about to enter a world beyond the five "known" senses, which offers you, as you will find out later, the data bank of infinite information. We will travel the universe that exists inside our bodies! As you rest, visualize your forearm. Touch the skin. Feel how firm it is, yet elastic and smooth. Keep on looking at it, while visualizing it getting larger and larger. Living with the opportunity that we can do anything in our minds, feel free to look inside this Gulliver-size skin. What is there? You might see a lot of muscles. Look into them, too. They consist of thousands of muscle fibers, containing many bundles of overlapping thick and thin filaments, which administer the muscle's movements. At this level, the muscles still feel firm to touch, however, as we go deeper, the environment drastically changes. It becomes softer and thinner. The delicate layers of cells on this level contain mainly water.

Let's take a closer look at one of the many trillion cells that exist in our bodies. They are made up of countless molecules, which in turn host an enormous number of assorted atoms. If you are not familiar with the atomic structure, you may compare it to the solar system: The sun would be the nucleus of the atom, while the planets would represent the electrons. The distance between the sun and the planets is tremendous in comparison to the size of the planets, as is the distance between the nucleus and the electrons that circle the space around it. If we could magnify the nucleus to the size of the head of a needle, the closest electron to it would be miles away! So, what is between them? Nothing. Just the force that holds them together. This is the energy level of our bodies. This is the energy level of everything known!

As you see, even though we appear solid, we are pure energy beings consisting of the same elements as the whole Universe!

One of the barriers we have to pass when we wish to understand our energy nature is to realize that there are more than five senses. We use five senses because we were taught to use five senses! Does it make sense? Our sixth sense, the most delicate, has been suppressed since we were born. We have been shown how to touch things, how to see, how to taste, how to smell and how to hear, but we have never had the chance to learn how to do all these things without our physical bodies. The sub-conscious was allowed to die! Occasionally, we are in touch with it, mainly through dreams, or possibly through some hunch, but we don't understand it, and we don't even try to resolve it. What if you could have a clear picture every time you experience a de-ja vu? Wouldn't it be nice to know about something even before it happens? How about if you could use your dreams to solve some problems? I'll go further than that: Can you imagine solving all your health problems without any medication?! Yes, it is possible! And a large portion of it is already accomplished through biotherapy.[1]

---

[1]Originally called bioenergy-therapy, it has been shortened for convenience.

In definition, **biotherapy is the scientific manipulation of the energy fields of the body.** With this technique the door is open to the ultimate doctor - the doctor within us!

It has been known for a long time that all matter is surrounded by a certain magnetic energy-field, which carries all the information about the given object.

There has been an experiment involving vitamin C, in which the energy-field information of the vitamin was transferred to pure water. Subsequently, this water was used to treat illnesses caused by deficiency of vitamin C. The unimaginable happened. It was as effective as if it had been done with real chemically developed vitamin C tablets, except - in our case - there were no tablets at all!

THE AURA

To learn more about our energy nature, first we have to understand the concept of the Aura. We've heard of this word so many times, but mostly through some mysterious psychics, telling us about our future while mentioning our "good" or "bad" auras, or on certain religious paintings. We may have been led to the false conclusion that this "thing" exists only in some eccentric individual's imagination. The aura is much more than that. Its existence is undeniable. The word itself originates from the Latin "aura", which means breath, or in a wider sense, emanation.

Emanation is the exact word we are looking for.

In the Soviet Union Semyon and Valentina Kirlian developed a photographical method which enables us to make pictures of high-frequency electromagnetic fields. With this discovery, it is believed, they found a way to photograph the human aura. On these pictures the aura is shown as an ever-changing bright light around the skin, with little sparkles on the edges. This light, or electromagnetic field, is present around every living being. Moreover, inanimate matter has an aura, too. However, while the inorganic aura is always even, the pictures show a great change and fluctuation in the auras of the living tissues. It has also been discovered that the bright light on these images gradually dims as the life leaves the body. For instance, we can see the phases of the changes in the aura of a fresh leaf as it slowly fades and finally dries up. It has also been observed that from a Kirlian - picture of a fingertip, we can follow the changes in an individual's health.

Furthermore, the advanced technology will enable us to make predictions about someone's health through Kirlian-photography, because our energy fields react faster to changes than our physical bodies! In some cases this has already been achieved. This subject will be discussed in the following chapters.

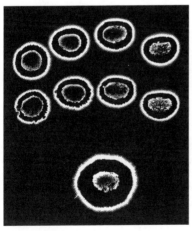

Kirlian photograph of the author's right fingertips.
-The top exposure shows the aura in total rest. It is nice and even, with no breaks - a healthy aura.
-The second exposure shows the aura during negative thinking, or anger. The changes are significant, showing breakage and asymmetry in the energy field.
-The third exposure is a picture of the middle finger only, taken while the author was concentrating on sending (or radiating) bioenergy. A huge difference in the size of the aura. It shows that you are actually gaining energy while radiating - not losing it.[1]

---

[1]The photos are courtesy of Kathryn Wishlow from Fort Myers, Florida.

Basic explanation of the Kirlian hand photo:
*-The index finger represents the mental body, while physically it
equals the head and neck.*
*-The middle finger represents the physical body, while physically it
equals the upper body, from the throat to the solar plexus.*
*-The ring finger represents the emotional body, while physically it
equals the area from the solar plexus to the hips.*
*-The pinky represents the spiritual body, while physically it equals
the legs.*
*The Kirlian photograph of the fingers also shows the condition
of the acupuncture meridians which are connected to them.*

As long as we are discussing the auras, we must not forget
that there is more than one layer in the human energy field. In

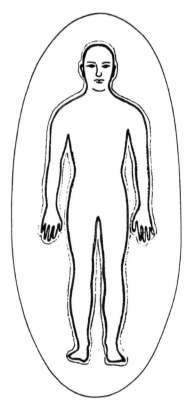

fact, there are seven
distinguishable layers of the
aura! While the first layer is
only about 1-2 mm thick and
fits tightly to the skin, the
seventh layer forms a perfect
egg-shape at a 2-3 feet distance
around the body. This,
however, varies from one
person to another.

According to people who
can see auras, every layer has
its own specific color, which
makes more sense if we
presume that there is a close
connection between the aura
and the chakras, which are
energy centers throughout the
body.

The idea of the chakras was
born in ancient India,
thousands of years ago, but
even today it is hard to prove

The first and the last layer of the aura

their existence. Some sophisticated instruments are able to register a concentration of the electromagnetic field at the areas where the chakras are presumably located, but there is no strong evidence of them in reality. However, in practice, many claim that these energy centers are there, indeed. From personal experience I can calmly say, "They are right!" Later on, you might feel them, too.

There are seven major chakras located on the midline of the trunk. Their colors are:
-Red   -first or base chakra
-Orange   -second or sacral chakra
-Yellow   -third or solar plexus chakra
-Green   -fourth or heart chakra
-Light Blue   -fifth or throat chakra
-Dark Blue   -sixth or ajna chakra
-White or Violet   -seventh or crown chakra

Each chakra governs a different part of the body:
-First chakra - adrenals, spinal column and kidneys.
-Second chakra - gonads, reproductive system.
-Third chakra - pancreas, stomach, liver, gall bladder, nervous system.
-Fourth chakra - thymus gland, heart, blood, vagus nerve, circulatory system.
-Fifth chakra - thyroid gland, bronchials, vocal apparatus, lungs, alimentary canal.
-Sixth chakra - pituitary gland, lower brain, left eye, ears, nose nervous system.
-Seventh chakra - pineal gland, upper brain, right eye.
In addition, there are twenty-one secondary chakras, too.

Their side-view resembles a funnel or a small tornado, getting wider as they go further from the body. At the last layer of the aura they can reach a diameter of more then a foot!

The role the chakras and the aura play in our health will be discussed in the next chapters.

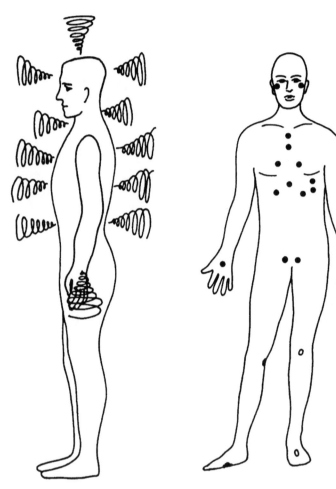

The seven major chakras   *21 secondary chakras*

HISTORY OF BIOTHERAPY

Healing through laying on of hands is probably as old as human history itself. Prehistoric man was soothing his pain by licking his wounds, grasping or rubbing the sore areas of his body, and holding his crying child, instinctively placing the bioenergy at the location where it was needed.

Unfortunately, we have no written documentation of when people first realized the existence of this life-force that flows in our bodies, but it has been mentioned throughout history. It is known that priests in ancient Egypt, Syria, Babylon and Palestine were successfully using different types of healing methods. One of the main procedures was laying on of hands. In ancient Greece healing through touch was a very important technique that was mentioned for the first time at about the fifth century B.C. Even Hippocrates, the father of the modern medicine, was a great promoter of the healing touch.

The real art of the touchless healing was developed in ancient China and India by recognizing the "life-forces" in the body calling them "chi" (pronounced: "chee") and "prana", respectively.

From the very beginning curing and healing were usually the duties of priests. Chinese priests concluded some strange things:

Soldiers who were stabbed at some specific areas of their legs, suddenly got rid of their headaches, stomachaches or backaches. That was the beginning of acupuncture. Archaeologists discovered sharp stones from approximately

10000-4000 B.C. which could have been used as acupuncture tools! That was possibly when they learned about the energy fields of the body. Acupuncture grew more sophisticated at the time of the legendary Huang Ti, the "Yellow Emperor" (about 2697-2596 B.C.), who can also be credited for developing some massage techniques, breathing exercises, moxibustion, etc. The Chinese had knowledge about the circulatory system nearly two thousand years before its "real" discoverer, the Englishman William Harvey!

All traditional Chinese healing methods are based on the concept of the Chi (Qi), the life-force that is everywhere: inside our bodies as well as all around the universe. The energies are made of two basic opposites, the Yin and the Yang. They originally meant the shady and sunny side of the hill. These are two complementary ideas that cannot exist one without the other. There is always Yin in Yang, and there is always Yang in Yin. Yin is the night, the shade, the cold, the calmness, the weak, the receiving, the tender, the feminine; while Yang is the opposite: the day, the light, the warmth, the moving, the strong, the radiating, the giving, the solid, the masculine. In visible forms, matter is a locally, temporarily condensed Chi in the state of rest. That way the Yang is the sky, the radiation; while the Yin is the earth, the solid matter. The whole universe is under the influence of the Chi, the "cosmic breath". Everything is in the state of dynamic and constant change and fluctuation of the opposite powers. Based on this theory, everything has to have a balance of the Yin and Yang in order to be in harmony with the universe. That means if the energies are in balance in our bodies, we are healthy. Biologically, the Chi can be called inner energy, life-force, bioenergy. If, for some reason, this energy flow gets into difficulties in the body, it will be out of balance and will result in illness.

The traditional Chinese medicine divides the reasons for illness in two large groups: inner and outer reasons. The inner reasons are primarily the emotions. Happiness, anger, sorrow, fearfulness, hard mental work, can all result in changes in the body. A prolonged negative emotional condition may sooner or later result in ailment. The outer reasons are described by the weather (warm, cold, dry, humid, or any other), food (which also has the characteristics of Yin and Yang), etc.

We can see the essential meaning of this theory, that Chinese medicine is not treating only the sick parts of the body, but the body as a whole, the equilibrium of the biologic and energy systems. This is what we call holistic healing.

When we talk about traditional Chinese medicine, we have to mention two more areas: T'ai Chi and Qi Gong. These are exercise systems which are designed and are executed in order to restore and maintain the Yin-Yang balance and the energy flow in the body. There are a lot of similarities between these two exercise systems and the Chinese martial art, Kung Fu, because they have the same roots. Even martial arts pays a lot of attention to the Chi. It can be concentrated in one part of the body and make the movements, hits, punches, kicks much more powerful. Breaking bricks needs more speed and control of the Chi than pure muscular strength.

Although T'ai Chi, as a martial art, was developed a very long time ago, it wasn't taught to any students but blood relations within a few families in the old China. Thanks to the Yang family, which started teaching others about hundred and fifty years ago, T'ai Chi became popular all over the world. Millions of people found the benefits of this exercise. It is a low-impact, light cardiovascular exercise system that does not require a lot from the practitioner, however it gives a great workout for the muscular system, the joints, the respiratory system, and especially provides a great mental alertness. The motions are based on principles of focus and balance with the emphasis on breathing. That is why it is called the "moving meditation". It involves shifting the body-weight from leg to leg relatively slowly, while the arms and legs sweep in front and beside the body. This weight-shift can be better understood by knowing that one leg resembles the Yin and the other the Yang. It is one of the best stress-reduction methods in our fast-

T'ai Chi

paced world. By practicing T'ai Chi for a long time, one can get to a state where balancing the energy can be done consciously. My T'ai Chi students learn how to feel and see the energy field around their bodies usually at their first or second class!

Qi Gong went a little further. While practicing this exercise also restores and maintains the body energy, it can also get to a level where the practitioner is able to give off some of his own energy to restore other people's energy equilibrium. The whole process can be (and is usually) done without any touch. Qi Gong is a very serious healing method even in modern China. Its original name, Kong Jin Qi Gong, literally means Empty Force Breathing Exercise. The modern Qi Gong was developed by the famous master, Huang Ren-Zhong, based on the movements of Shaolin and other types of martial arts. He has been practicing this art since he was seven years old. Because he can heal some illnesses that modern medicine can't, people call him the "Magic Hands". There are a lot of legendary stories about him, but the most sensational was at the congress of the Qi Gong practitioners in Jinan, China in 1983 when he was treating a fifteen year old girl who had been paralyzed for over three years because of spinal meningitis. The master put her on a chair and from about three feet away, lifted his hands towards her. After remaining motionless for about five minutes, he started moving his fingers. After another five minutes the girl's fingers started moving, together with her legs. Half an hour later the girl started sweating and got red in the face. After three days of treatments, she could stand on her own feet and was also able to move her fingers. This story demonstrates the exceptional powers of Master Huang, however anyone can master this art to a certain degree.

Qi Gong and biotherapy are two very similar energy-balancing methods. They were born in two different times, two different cultures, and two different continents, but they both use the same energy.

The Holy Bible also contains accounts of several miraculous healings throughout history that could be attributed to some sort of "energy".

In Europe history of the healing touch is much younger than in Asia, but is still significant. As already mentioned, the ancient Greeks were strong believers in energy-healing. Solon, Plinius and Vergilius mentioned the "Healing Hands" many times. Hippocrates was also a great healer.

By 1530 in Western Europe the well-known physician and alchemist of the middle-ages, Theophrastus Paracelsus, had already proclaimed that people could greatly influence each other only by their life-force. Using his teachings, J.B. van Helmont talked about the magnetic forces in people. Later, William Maxwell became known by his "Sympathetic" treatments, which also put the emphasis on magnetism (De Medicina Magnetica-1769).

Arguably the most important work in the field of biomagnetism at that time was done by the famous 18th century German doctor, Franz Anton Mesmer. Mesmer caused one of the biggest uproars in medical circles of his time. He received his doctorate in 1766 in Vienna with a controversial doctoral thesis, in which he mentioned the magnetic qualities of the living beings. He developed the term "Animal Magnetism".

According to his theory, every living being has some magnetic attributes that greatly control health and life in general. Disease resulted from an obstacle to the flow of the magnetic fluid.

He first tried to influence some illnesses by putting magnets on different areas of the body. Later, he developed magnetic tubs, where sick patients would take a bath in a specially designed bathtub in which the water was previously treated with, or contained magnets.

Mesmer claimed that the magnetic current (or in his words: fluid) in living beings could increase or decrease the quality, flexibility, density, stability, irritability, magnetism, etc. of inorganic as well as organic forms. Following the experiments with the magnetic water, he realized that he could get better results by using his bare hands. He had quite a few followers of his theory. Instead of bleeding and applying purgatives (methods of contemporary medicine of that time), Mesmerists ran their fingers over their patients' bodies, searching out spots where they could add the Mesmeric fluid in order to restore the natural balance of the energy.

One of the most significant healings using his hands was done on the pianist, Lady von Paradies, who was famous in the court of Queen Maria Theresa of Austria. She had been blind since the age of four because of a paralysis of the optical nerves. The controversy of the method was so intense, that her parents were forced to remove her from Mesmer's care.

Another meaningful case involved the director of the Osvald Academy in Munich, Germany. Mesmer saved him from the paralysis which followed a stroke. After this incident he moved to Paris, where he opened a free clinic for his patients. It is a fact that Mesmerism was effective with nervous disorders. Mesmer was very careful about documenting his work. There are hundreds of notarized case histories and documents left behind him.

Mesmer had a lot of enemies in medical circles because of his controversial methods, and his work was even forgotten for a while, but he gave an important jump-start to the European energy-awakenings. Today, Mesmer's name is mostly known through the term "Mesmerizing", although it has lost its original meaning, which was a method of hypnosis. Actually, the most recognition he has received from modern science is for his work in the field of hypnosis, thanks to his followers, who developed "Mesmerically Induced Hypnosis" in 1784. We'll get back to Mesmer later when a practical use of one of his therapies will be explained.

After a long silence, the electromagnetic characteristics of the human body re-emerge at the end of the 19th and the beginning of the 20th century, with the appearance of studies about Yoga, which at that time was a mystery to Europe. The first books about the touch-less healing show up, for instance, The Healing Magnetism by Van Hess Stiemann. Studies about Yoga masters started a chain of experiments in parapsychology.

One of the most important circumstances was the visual conception of the human energy field, which was first photographed in 1939. Today, this method is known as Kirlian Photography. In a high-frequency electric field it is possible to make a picture of so-called Kirlian-radiation, which is an electromagnetic field produced by the body. This field is made partly of a low-intensity magnetic field, partly of an electric field which has a frequency of about 10 Hz, an infrared radiation from 8-14 microns, and super-high frequency waves in the 18-330 cm wave band.

In the middle of our century most of the work in the field of bioenergy was done by the scientists of the Eastern Block countries, especially the former Soviet Union. There was a significant growth in the number of so-called psychic healers, as well as people with different parapsychological abilities. Most of us have seen the televised documentary from the sixties in which a Russian lady demonstrates her mind-boggling parapsychological abilities. She was able to move objects on the table, make the compass spin around, etc.

The same and even more confusing abilities are displayed by the famous Uri Geller, who is known to the world by his demonstrations of bending spoons, keys and other metals. Not many people know about his gifts as a psychic or telepath, who can "read" other individuals' minds. His demonstrations include asking someone to draw a simple picture, which he would later reproduce almost perfectly without ever seeing it. Many experiments on him, trying to figure out the nature of his gift, have failed. His competence wasn't challenged even when he was in a Faraday-cage. Mr. Geller will definitely remain a mystery for a while.

One of the most famous healers of the second half of the 20th century is certainly Dzuna Davitashvili, also from the Soviet Union. Her healing capabilities are practically endless. She was (and still is) the subject of hundreds of experiments. Dzuna (as she is known to everyone) has apparently the largest file-collection in the history of energy-healing. She has had thousands of patients with basically every medical history imaginable, and her results are amazing. There is practically nothing that is impossible for this woman. Thousands of cases have been authenticated on paper or on video tape. She has treated a lot of well-known people, among them the late president of the Soviet Union, Leonid Brezhnev.

The reason this country put so much energy in the study of the paranormal is very simple: In communist ideals there is no concept of god. Because of that, Soviet scientists have had the assignment to prove that behind all these miraculous healings, there is some physical explanation. They pretty much did it. They measured all the imaginable electromagnetic features of the body: direct current, alternating current, capacity, inductivity, conductivity, resistance, etc. After recording all the Amperes, Volts, nano Farads, milli Henries, Herz's and Ohms, they came to a conclusion of how to tell a difference between ordinary people and people born to be healers. That wasn't all. They could make a distinction between healthy and sick individuals, between good givers and good receivers, and much more. They were the first to mention the term "Bioplasma". Bioplasma is the same energy as the QI, Chi, Prana, bioenergy, or animal magnetism, however, it was the first one to have a scientific name in our century.

In the middle of the 1980's in Yugoslavia, there was another name on the rise: Zdenko Domancic, a Croatian from the Adriatic island of Ugljan. He seemingly appeared from nowhere and suddenly became the main subject of all the newspapers in the country. Domancic became famous in a very short time, because of the miraculous healings he had performed on thousands of people. The island was instantly invaded by sick people, who couldn't find help in contemporary medicine.

The uproar about Domancic led to a serious examination of his abilities. Zagreb, Croatia in January, 1985 was the place and time of the largest exam in Yugoslavia of the frontiers of the human healing capabilities. Hundreds of people of medicine participated directly or indirectly in this examination. The subject had to be some problem the modern science hadn't yet solved. They chose gangrene. The tests ran for almost half a year, and the results were amazing. Some of the numerous patients virtually walked away, even though they had scheduled dates for amputations!

The following are the words of Dr. Josip Cicek, specialist of internal medicine and epidemiology: "By all my medical knowledge and experience, R. P. was supposed to be dead in 48 hours, and he is alive, and he is even getting better! No, this is simply unbelievable. If someone had told me about this, I wouldn't believe it! Either they taught me wrong for decades, or this is a real miracle what Zdenko Domancic just did."[1]

---

[1]From <u>With Bioenergy to Health</u> by Drasko Acimovic

This experiment started a whole new history of healing in that country.

At the same time other European countries have had great interest in this science. England and Italy taught biotherapy even in colleges (Yugoslavia joined them later by certifying biotherapists at the People's University of Belgrade). Biotherapists became part of some medical institutions and hospitals, along with dowsers and other representatives of alternative medicine.

The United States has its own history of healers as well. Native Americans have been conducting spiritual healing through rituals way before the arrival of Columbus, and who hasn't heard of Edgar Cayce, the world famous mystic and clairvoyant? Born on a small farm in Kentucky, he was expected to live a "normal life" serving others. It all changed when, as a relatively young man, he unexpectedly discovered a strange psychic ability to diagnose illness in his "sleep", and to prescribe treatments as well. His accomplishment in healing his family and thousands of others has made him a phenomenon, still being mentioned and admired. There are several books available about his life, healing, and remedies.

In the early 70's, Dolores Krieger and Dora Kunz developed the first significant effort to bring healing to the reach of the general public by developing their system, the Therapeutic Touch (TT). It became so popular, that it has been taught in over seventy countries in the world, mainly in colleges, universities and schools of nursing. There are also several books and seminars available on this subject.

Today, several healing methods are practiced and taught all over the world, giving relief to thousands of people.

MEETING WITH THE INCREDIBLE

It has been over ten years since I heard of biotherapy for the first time, thanks to the sensation-seeking media. There was a report about it on TV, and later on a few articles appeared in a couple of newspapers. At that time, they didn't mention it under this name, rather it was referred to as "psychic healing" or just "healing". Although the articles were written in serious papers and in a solemn manner, my first reaction was the same as everybody else's in my country: Yeah, right! They want me to believe that someone got healed from a deadly disease just by this guy waving his hands around him!

I had heard of acupuncture, and I knew a few pressure points, and years of studying martial arts had given me an insight to the power of the Chi, but this was a little bit too much. At the time I was a student at an electro-technical high school, and I had enough trouble understanding the electrons that punch and kick each other to send that electricity through the wire. Now, they were telling me that this electromagnetic current in our bodies is able to travel to someone else's body without any connection?! O.K., Nikola Tesla had an idea of sending electricity over long distances with no wires, but to my knowledge that had never been accomplished. And this was the human body we were talking about!

As time passed by, more and more stories hit the news and went mouth-to-mouth (the main media in the country), so no one could really ignore them. "Miraculous Healings", "I can

19

walk again!", "A few movements around the head, and the migraine is gone!", and such headlines just couldn't be ignored.

I was very open-minded, thanks to my chemist father and my artist/teacher mom. I had read about ancient civilizations, pyramids, Mayan ruins, airports in the Andes, UFO's and other mysteries way before my first Tolstoy or Shakespeare, so it shouldn't have been a problem opening my mind to such a thing as Energy Healing. But, there was no available literature about anything like that.

My first **real** experience came a year later, when my father's old friend paid us a visit for a week-end. I had known him for a while; he was a publisher for a nature magazine in Belgrade, land owner, and an enthusiast of natural healing and herbology, as well as a great guy. For me, he was only Uncle Laci. His visit changed my life forever.

The first day I didn't have much time to talk to him, because I had to do a difficult drawing for an architecture class I was attending at the college. I had just started my studies in Industrial Safety Engineering, so I was overloaded with assignments. I was close to finishing my work (and passing out from exhaustion), when I heard my father's loud laughter from the living room. Uncle Laci was a great joker, so I thought he was giving a good entertainment to my parents. "Well, I can't miss that", went through my mind, so I joined them. But, there were no jokes. My dad's laughter was just heavy sarcasm.

Apparently, Uncle Laci was demonstrating the power of his subconscious by using a small pendulum, and my father's disbelief was the cause of his laughter. The pendulum is the main tool of dowsers, and is used to bring out the subconscious, or the "sixth" sense, Laci explained. "If you put it in your right hand and concentrate heavily on the word YES, it will start spinning in one direction, and if you concentrate on NO-the opposite direction."

"What the hell, let's have some fun", I thought, so I gave it a try. Suddenly, my father turned serious. The pendulum started spinning in my hands like crazy! And my brain was spinning with it! Needless to say, we were speechless, but that wasn't the end of it.

The next demonstration didn't require a tool. It was about the ENERGY! Uncle Laci used what he called bioenergy and ESP (extrasensory perception) to find the areas of our bodies where there was a problem, and to "fix" them. He went around each of us, one at a time, in some funny, pantomimic, but gentle manner, making movements as if he was stroking the air a few inches from our bodies. What a strange experience! We could actually feel something. There was warmth, tingling, pressure, and a lot of surprise. Wow! So, this is it!

Following the demonstration, Uncle Laci explained to me how I could do the same, and added that he had a strong feeling I was a natural talent. "Not many people can make the pendulum spin like that! There has to be something special about this kid!" Those words were enough. I was convinced I could do something special with myself.

We spent the rest of the evening talking about bioenergy, drinking in every word from Uncle Laci's mouth.

The night ahead was one of the worst in my life. I couldn't sleep at all! I had a bad headache, my head was spinning, and I was sick to my stomach. I was just tossing around and cursing at every bark in the neighborhood. Next morning, my mom was complaining of the same. We knew right a way, the reason for our bad sleep was the treatment received the previous night. It took me years though, to understand why. Laci was still in baby's shoes for biotherapy and instead of just balancing our energy fields, he gave us energy, much more than our bodies needed. That caused the pain and all the suffering we had for a night. My father was O.K. because the only treatment he had received was to his legs.

Regardless, Uncle Laci will stay in my memory as the person who opened my eyes and put me on the right track. A couple of weeks after his departure, I received three books on natural healing that were published by the company he worked for. They were not bad for a start, but I was craving for more. I didn't have to wait long. A month later, while I was on a lunch break at the college, I decided to check out the nearby bookstore. And there it was: My first serious bioenergy book. <u>Bioenergy - A World Without Disease</u> by Branislav and Ljubisa Stojanovic. It was quite a reading! For the moment most of my questions were answered.

After I was finished with the book, my hunger for more information just grew stronger. I became a regular in every bookstore in the town. Biotherapy books were hard to find, so I started reading anything about human energy fields that was available. Old Chinese and Indian traditional medicine wasn't a mystery for me anymore. I even went abroad to Hungary to seek books there. Hungarian wasn't strange for me, it was my native language.

It went on like that for quite a while. In the meantime, I was practicing on every person available. My whole family and friends became Guinea pigs for my experiments. At first they were teasing me, mimicking my biotherapy-movements every time I would show up, but after a few headaches were gone, everybody accepted my strange hobby. Yes, it was just a hobby for a long time...

Then I saw a documentary about the superstar of all the healers, Zdenko Domancic, a Croatian working wonders with his small team of healers on the Adriatic island of Ugljan. I had heard of him before, but this was the first time I had seen him at work. It blew my mind! He was bending, pushing, and moving people without touching them! And more! All the sessions were public, in front of hundreds of people. Sometimes he would even work on more than just one person at the same time. But those movings... How did he do that?! How could he heal such a crowd? The island was swamped with thousands of people every day! It was almost like the pilgrimage to the nearby Medjugorje for the appearance of the

Virgin Mary. The small island became an international attraction, adding a new notion to our vocabulary: Health Tourism.

I was so impressed by this man that I decided to make biotherapy my career. I tried to get in touch with him by every accessible means of communication, but without success. The latest I heard was that he moved his "practice" somewhere else, but no one could tell me where.

Several weeks after the documentary, my mom was complaining of a backache. Naturally, I jumped in right away to ease the pain and, of course, to show off with my skill. I told her to stand still and relax, then I started manipulating the energy around her back. At that time I thought the best way to take off the pain is to pull out the "bad" energy, so all I did was the "pulling movements". And then the unthinkable happened: My mom started bending backwards! At first, I thought she was just kidding, but when I saw her face I knew it was I who had moved her. I was out of my mind! I felt the power within wanting to burst out.

The next few days I didn't do anything else but try to move all my friends without touching them. Finally, the teasing stopped for good. I couldn't affect all of them, but the few I could was enough to prove that I wasn't joking.

One Friday afternoon, my best friend from the neighborhood came over with a week old newspaper. He excitedly pointed out to me an article about a professor at a Belgrade university who was conducting measurings of the bio-energy fields. The article ended with the date and the place of the next measurement. It was scheduled for Saturday afternoon in Belgrade. I got so excited that I dropped all my plans for the weekend, and the next morning I set out on a train to Belgrade.

I arrived right on time. Professor Slobodan Bucic had just started his speech. He briefly explained some facts about the bioenergy, and how he was going to measure our fields. It wasn't a big deal. There were no super instruments or laser lights. We had to put our hands on some copper plates, called bio-accumulators, while regular instruments would measure the voltage, the intensity of current, impedance, capacity, inductivity, resistance, frequency, temperature, and who knows what else. By comparing the data with the previous evaluations he had conducted on thousands of people, professor Bucic could tell who was gifted with the ability to expand the bio-energy level to a higher plane.

I was the last one to receive the results, and my excitement just accelerated when he pulled me over to tell me the news. "You my friend, are one of ten thousand, according to my statistics, and if I were you, I would consider changing my career. You should be a biotherapist!" Imagine the look on my face! That was exactly what I wished to hear! I said it was fine, but the only man I wanted to learn from was Mr. Domancic, and I didn't have the slightest idea where I could find him. "Oh, that's not a problem, he is a very good friend of mine, and right now, he is working a half an hour away from here." I was overwhelmed by excitement. After a short pause we got in the car and drove to nearby Pancevo to meet Zdenko, who had moved his practice to a large hotel, that way avoiding the formation of massive crowds on the streets.

When we arrived, he was in the middle of the sessions. It was amazing to see so many people patiently waiting for their turn. I can't even name how many different problems they had come with. I saw some in wheelchairs, some holding their backs, some with their babies, or grandparents... These were all people who couldn't find help in modern medicine. Later I found out that there was no charge for the treatments, but everybody would leave as much money as they could afford at the end of the week. The sessions were conducted five days a week, approximately six to eight hours a day, with two hours of lunch break. There would be a new group of about 150 every week!

Zdenko was handling the situation well. He had three students working with him, and a secretary who was admitting and registering every new patient, but most of the labor fell on his back. He was very serious about every case he received, breaking the silence only from time to time to joke around with the astonished people that he had just moved or bent. People sitting around in the large circular room couldn't take their eyes off him. It was a group therapy at the same time. Everybody had to separate their feet and hands, turning the palms of their hands up, this way receiving the needed bio-energy that filled the room. Some headaches were gone just by sitting in that position! Other than that, everyone was very relaxed (except their first day), enjoying the soothing music and some quiet conversations. I sat there until the end of the sessions, just mesmerized by that man.

After the room emptied, professor Bucic introduced me to Zdenko. "So, this is the next big healer" he said, while squeezing my shaky hands. Then the conversations started and went on for days. I learned more in that one week than in months of previous studies. I was taught how to balance the energy field in only minutes, how to give or take off large amounts of energy in a very short time, how to approach different health problems, and even how to move people very easily. But, most of all, I learned how to be very confident.

After returning home, I continued my studies at the college, just to get it over with. I was close to the end anyway, and it was a good way to please my parents and to prove to myself that I could do it. Of course, this time I would meditate before I would sit down to study, which helped me reduce the study time. I would learn everything in two hours that others needed to study for an entire day.

In the meantime, my studies in the field of biotherapy became more and more intense. I had read all the biotherapy books published both in Yugoslavia and Hungary, plus books on every related subject. All the free time I had, was spent

practicing my skills on friends, relatives, and on anyone who
needed my help. Very soon, my book of case studies was filled
up, making me more experienced every day by giving me the
opportunity to compare the related situations.

After a time, I became very popular in my town, not just
because I was doing the treatments for free, but because there
were very serious results of my work. I helped a lot of people
get rid of migraine headaches, asthma, diabetes, etc., which
gave me more confidence for my upcoming exam. I was getting
ready for my certification in biotherapy, which took place in
Pancevo, during the same week I had to defend my diploma-
work at the college. That was the period of my life with the
least sleep I've ever had.

By the time the day of the exam came, I had mastered every
aspect of bioenergy and biotherapy. I had so many sessions
behind me that I felt I could not fail.

The examination lasted almost a whole week and went very
smoothly. I was proven to be gifted last time, now I had to
prove that I could use that gift in the correct way. At the
beginning of the week, Mr. Domancic assigned me with ten
patients who I had to work on for five days. All I can remember
now is that among those ten, I had one person with asthma, one
with bad headaches, one with some throat problem, and one
with a bad back. They were also my big successes. All of their
symptoms disappeared! The other six people felt much better,
too! That was the happiest week of my life! (Two days later I
defended my diploma-work at the college with the highest
grade.)

After returning home, I took a long, well-deserved vacation,
and followed by opening my own biotherapy-practice. It was
more than a success! While the first month I had about thirty
patients, two months later I had that many a day! The word of
mouth is very strong in Yugoslavia, and I gave them a good
reason to use it. In a short period of time I earned a great
reputation in an area of at least fifty miles. I had a very colorful

clientele, from all walks of life. A lot of people I treated were of various medical professions, among them some famous psychiatrists, medical doctors and dentists. That shows how much biotherapy is accepted in Europe.

My career as a biotherapist in Yugoslavia ended when I came to the USA for a vacation. Right after I arrived in 1991, one of the dirtiest wars of the century started in my old country. It was against all my beliefs to be a part of it, so I decided to start a new life in a new country.

Since then I have received my certificate from the Venice School of Massage (earning the money for it as a pizza-boy and as a Teppan chef in a Japanese steak house) and I have been working as a Licensed Massage Therapist, massage teacher, T'ai Chi instructor, and of course a biotherapist. Biotherapy is not very well known in the USA, so I have taken a lot of time educating the public about it by doing lectures and writing articles.

I hope, with the help of other energy-balancing techniques as therapeutic touch, polarity therapy, reiki, Qi Gong, etc., biotherapy will become a regular therapeutic treatment for the benefit of the American people.

Zdenko Domancic (sitting on a chair in the middle) and his students, with the author on the right. The picture is from 1990.

EXPERIENCING THE AURA

Can you believe that you are able to feel or even see the aura? Well, you better, because that is the truth! Ninety percent of people are capable of perceiving bio-energy after their first attempt! It is really not a big deal. We don't need any special tools or instruments, nor any exceptional psychic powers. It is just a matter of practice and a little concentration.

Before you start the following exercises, assume a comfortable position. It doesn't matter if you are sitting, standing or lying down. The main idea is to relax. Take a few deep breaths, and clear your mind. You will learn how to...

FEEL YOUR AURA

1) Hold up your hands in a comfortable position in front of your chest. Let your elbows hang, and relax your shoulders. Keep your hands about 12 inches apart, and loosen your fingers. Now, imagine that you are holding a very light ball. Close your eyes and look at your fictitious ball. Feel how smooth it is. After about ten seconds, start playing with it: Compress it to about 10 inches then release it back a couple of inches. Do this a few times using very small, fast movements.

Can you feel the resistance? Isn't it just like playing with magnets, when you put the same polarities opposite each other?

The feeling you are experiencing is not because you have a good imagination, but because you have found the edges of one of the layers of your aura!

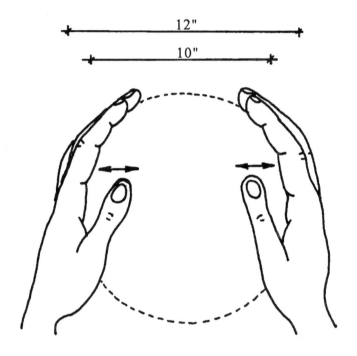

2) Now, do the same, however, this time bring your hands closer together, all the way to an inch away from each other. It is a very interesting sensation if you do it gradually, inch by inch, letting your hands go back a little bit after every advance. Can you feel the resistance increasing as your hands get closer? Let's "turn the magnet": Go the opposite way. Can you feel your hands pulling back to the center this time? Congratulations! You can feel your aura! You might even feel some heat or tingling in your hands as you practice.

Don't be discouraged if there is no sensation! You just need a little bit more concentration and practice.

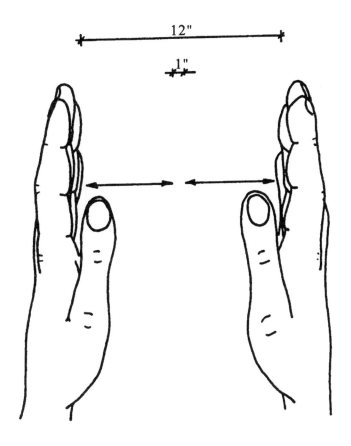

If nothing works, try this: Gently press the middle of each palm with the opposite hand's thumb, and try the exercises one more time. This is a proven way of increasing the perception in your hands, at least for the time you are developing this routine.

3) This time try to do circular movements on distances that vary from 1 to 12 inches. You will be able to feel the energy whirling around the centers of your palms. You can also accelerate the sensation by pressing the middle of your palms before you start this exercise.

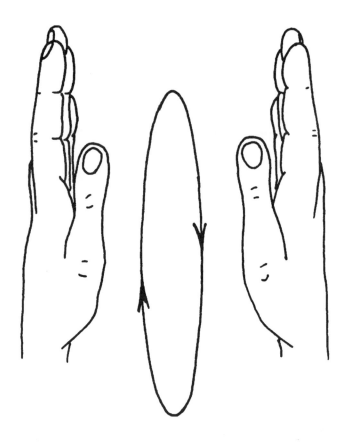

4) Let's go a step further. Use only one hand and the forefinger of the other. Start by establishing the feeling in the middle of your palm, holding the tip of your forefinger about an inch away. Again, you might feel a little heat, tingling, or pressure. Now, make small circles around that spot. If you still have the feeling, gradually increase the distance, and at the same time increase the diameter of the circles. See how far can you go without losing the "touch".

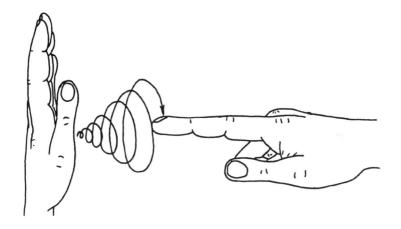

5) Now, use only the two forefingers to do the same exercise. In addition, you can circle the fingers around each other keeping approximately an inch between them.

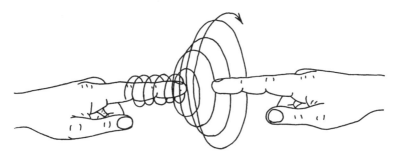

6) This exercise is very important for your further advancement. From your palm move one hand slowly up by your forearm, at about a 2 inch distance. Try it first on the more sensitive inside of the forearm. Travel with your hand up and down several times. Feel every little change in temperature or pressure. Indicate the spots that give you different impression. Continue the same on the outside of your forearm.

Remember, if you have ever had any injuries, those areas will still register in your energy field, and you will always be able to feel them.

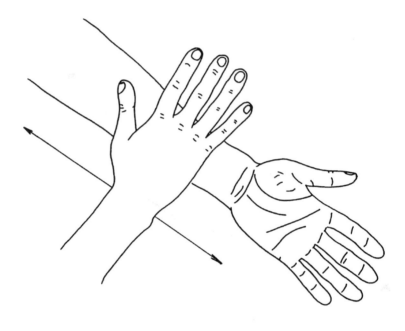

It would be very interesting and educating to do all of the above exercises with a partner. Exchange your impressions and practice the movements together. If you establish the feeling in your hands, you can continue exploring the whole aura of your partner. Try to find the areas where the energy is out of balance by getting different readings in your hands other than normal. It could be heat, cold, pressure, tingling, vibration, or other, depending on the individual. Don't try to manipulate the energy fields, yet. You might do more harm than good!

Now, you are ready to go to the next step. You will learn how to...

SEE YOUR AURA

Find a plain area on the wall or ceiling which is not too bright and not too dark. Don't look directly into any source of illumination, and for the best results, don't try these exercises in sunlight. If you have accomplished all of the above, you can start practicing.

7) Hold up your hands at eye level, palms facing you, with extended fingers. The distance between the tips of the fingers should be about 1-2 inches. Now comes the hard part. Look directly at the area between the fingertips. Try not to be distracted by staring at your fingers. Keep your eyes on the area between your fingertips! Watch it carefully. Can you see something between the opposing fingertips? It looks a little bit foggy, doesn't it? You may describe it as hazy, misty, smoggy, cloudy, blurry or any other way, the main thing is to see it. That "thing" is all around your fingers and your whole body as well! What you see is the first layer of your aura!

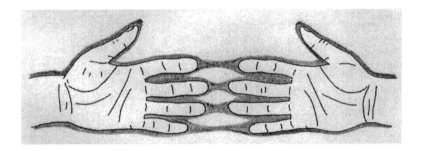

If you observe it carefully, you'll be able to see little funnel-like light beams coming out of your fingertips.

8) Now, oppose one hand with only the forefinger of the other. Slowly, move the forefinger up and down along the fingers, keeping the established distance. Can you see how the blurry beam from the forefinger connects with each of the fingertips of the opposing hand as it passes them? It even

connects to two at a time when it is between the fingers, forming a triangle that disappears as you move further.

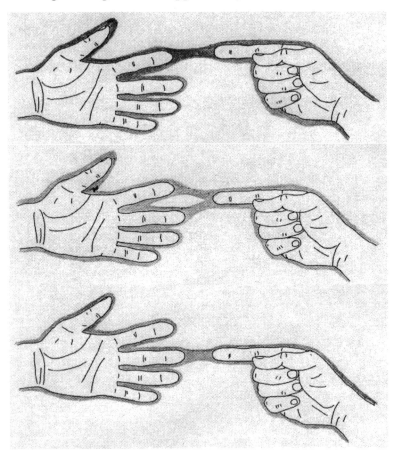

Experiment to see how far you can go before losing the beams, and if you can see anything when you put your palms against each other.

Do the same exercises with a partner and exchange your impressions!

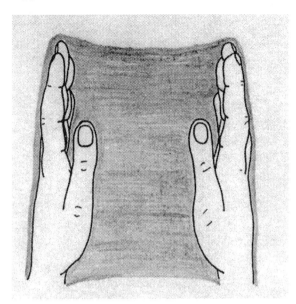

9) For the next exercise ask your partner to stand against a plain wall, and observe the area around his/her body, starting with the top of the head. Again, don't look directly at the body,

rather concentrate on the area around it. You should see the same blurry picture you have seen around your fingers. After some practice you'll be able to see a funnel of energy coming out of the top of your partner's head!

10) For another interesting experiment, ask your partner to stand against the wall, and observe his/her aura for a minute. Then let your partner quickly move out of your

sight line while you continue watching the same spot. You will still be able to see the aura for a few seconds, even though nobody stands there! That shows you how the energy field leaves its print anywhere you go.

If you really want to get serious about studying the aura, start observing other people's energy fields, as well. Note the differences in the aura during changes in their mood or health. If you go to a concert, don't miss the singers' auras. You will be surprised how large and intense they get during their performance!

In addition you can concentrate on other auras, not just human. Examine your pets, your plants, trees around the house, etc.

If you cut a leaf in half, you will still be able to see the so-called "phantom picture" for a while, which is a full aura of the leaf, even though half of it is not there anymore. After a few minutes the picture will change, leaving only a small beam of energy at the area of the missing part.

There are many other experiments you can do, just use your imagination. Although, it is really not so important to see the aura in order to manipulate it, the opportunities of exploring it are endless. Keep up with the challenge, and enjoy yourself!

LIVING ORGANISMS AND BIOENERGY
-Why do we get sick-

Bioenergy is a part of every living being. Without it, there is no life. Every atom of a living organism has its energy field, consequently, every molecule, cell, tissue, organ and organism has a complex energy field made up of these atoms. Our bodies are huge playgrounds of constantly changing electromagnetic charges. They run up and down, left and right, in all directions, like a curious child trying to be a part of all around it. This constant fluctuation is a universal law and is valid for everything, living or dead.

As we learned from the Chinese symbol of Yin and Yang, everything in the universe should be in balance, which is the case with our energy fields, too. We not only depend on our aura, the aura also depends on us. We hold the ticket to our health! If we let our energy field get out of control, the large changes in it may result in sickness.

So, we see, our aura should always be balanced. The first layer is always only a few millimeters to an inch away from the skin, while the last layer forms a perfect egg-shape about an arm's reach away from the body. Of course, as everything else, this distance also changes virtually every moment of our lives. However, as long as the changes are not significant, we have nothing to worry about, moreover, we don't even feel them. The problem starts when the deviations in the energy field are large, for they may lead to vital changes in our health.

But, what makes the energy change? Why is it that some people never get sick, while others can't live without medicine? Is there a physical reason to it, or is it all just in our minds? Is there a way to actually control these changes?

Many of these questions are so complex that we may never get the answers to them, although, in theory and on paper we do have most of the explanations. Some of the data about the human energy fields are already available through measuring the "regular" physical/electromagnetic attributes of the body, or through the controversial Kirlian photography. The rest is yet to come.

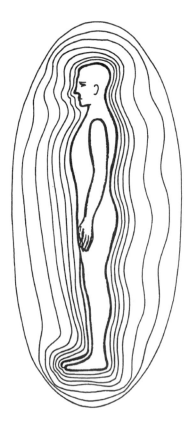

The healthy aura

So, let's see what it is that we know. How does the energy-change influence our system?

There are only two possible abnormalities associated with the aura: Excess energy or deficiency in the field, causing opposite reactions. Before discussing the problems, let's review how a healthy aura looks.

A healthy aura is like a shield to the body. It protects us as the immune system does, except it is all around, not just in our "physical" bodies. Every part of the shield should be the same distance from the skin, or in better words: every layer of our aura has its established distance from the body which should not change. As we already know the thickness of each layer, we can now approach the question: How do the changes in them influence our health?

DEFICIENCY OF BIOENERGY IN THE AURA

It is simple: If you lose bioenergy, your "shield" gets weaker, which means that you have less protection, and you are vulnerable to outer influences.

Losing energy itself does not make you sick, but being defenseless eventually does. It is like going out into freezing temperatures without proper clothing. The less clothes we have on, the sooner we get cold. The difference is that less bioenergy in our field does not always result in a physical weakness. It can also cause mental and emotional problems. It all depends on the individual and on the part of the aura having the deficiency.

Examining the aura provides some simple, but very logical conclusions to what the actual problem is. Some experienced biotherapists are able to make very accurate diagnoses just by touching parts of the aura for a few minutes.

Examples:

-Less energy around the middle of the thorax (middle of the back and the chest) usually means there is some problem with the lungs. Further examination may show if it is a cold, flu, bronchitis, asthma, or a smoker's lungs.

-Less energy around the eyes and the back of the head will of course, show a problem with the eyes.

-Less energy around the whole head may result in a mental weakness or fatigue.

-Less energy around any other section of the body will reveal a problem in that area.

Treatments of the energy-deficient areas always include giving bioenergy to the body and filling up the holes to a

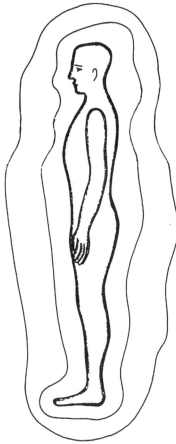

hundred percent of balance. After the energy field gets back to normal, the body is able to continue its natural function. It is able to heal itself! I can compare the procedure to giving someone a jump-start. If you buy a new car, and in the big celebration and three days of partying you forget your lights on, naturally, your battery dies. All I have to do is give you a jump-start to make it run. After that, your alternator will do its job - it will fill up the battery, and your trouble is over. The same happens to your body. If your "alternator" works, all you need is a "jump-start" to make the "engine run"!

Deficiency of bioenergy in the aura associated with the illness of the lungs

EXCESS BIOENERGY IN THE AURA

For a long time it was believed that the only possible cause of sickness was deficiency of the energy in the aura. This conception couldn't be further from the truth! All the pain we experience is caused by excess energy in that location! Whether it is induced by injury, some other physical cause, or by the concentration of the energy itself for some other reasons, pain is always closely associated with overabundance of the bioenergy.

In case of an injury we know how the body reacts: Sensory neurons transmit impulses to the spinal cord and brain from the afflicted area, resulting in pain, which is actually a warning to our brain to take care of that part of the body. The brain will instantly send another signal through the spine and the motor neurons which will conclude in a reflex reaction. This would be a simple "reflex arc". If the injury is more complex, it will result in a constant feeling of pain. The body's defense mechanism will try everything to "fix" the problem. It will produce fever, edema, etc., depending on the injury. At the same time it will send more bioenergy to the area, in order to speed up the recovery. And it occurs every time. There are no exceptions!

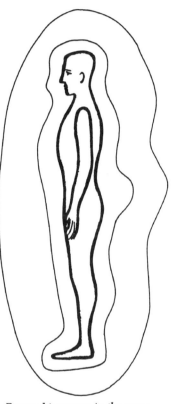

Excess bioenergy in the aura associated with low back pain

But, what if it is a headache? We get them without injuries all the time. The answer is simple: Most of the sensory neurons are located in the superficial tissues. We don't feel the internal organs. If there is a problem, we'll usually find out about it only by the body's reaction, not by pain. That is the situation with most of the headaches, too. We have no idea about the problem until we get one. The body protects our heads by sending extra energy to thicken the "shield". We can get rid of any headache in only minutes just by taking away the excess energy! That is the easiest part. The big enigma is the cause.

The treatment of the areas with surplus bioenergy always includes taking off the energy. As the aura gets back to normal, the pain vanishes. The result, again, depends on the nature of the cause. Sometimes one treatment is enough for a complete recovery, while other times it takes many sessions just to soothe the ache.

The question still remains: What alters the bioenergy? Without any doubt, I can say: Everything! The food we eat, the air we breathe, the weather, the environment, injuries, exercise, our thoughts... everything that is a part of our lives is a part of our bioenergy as well. Some influence it more, some less, but they all count.

THE INFLUENCE OF THE ENVIRONMENT

Have you noticed how your mood reacts to the changes in the weather? A nice, sunny day will always make you feel good and ready for everything, while a cold, cloudy, rainy day will just "drain your energy". Don't you experience more pleasure from a beautiful spring day than from a dark, grey, winter afternoon? Isn't it more delightful being somewhere in the mountains, breathing the clean air, than in a large, smoggy city? We all feel better and more secure in our own house surrounded with trees and a nice neighborhood, than in a rented apartment in the middle of a concrete-jungle.

These are only a few examples of how our mood pattern is influenced by the surroundings. There is nothing new about it, however, with our mood our energy changes, too. Rapidly! We are enclosed in a large box of different colors, smells, and air, and are very much under its dominion.

There are other, more powerful sources of negative influence to our energy system. They are indeed called **negative energy**, and are mainly creations of the modern society.

Computers, microwave ovens, televisions, etc., and the strongest ones - the electric cables and transformer stations, are all very forceful origins of negative energy. Staying in their field for long periods of time may gradually weaken our auras to alarming levels. There was a study done about people living in apartment buildings in which the transformer stations were located on the first floors of the buildings themselves. The percentage of heart-attacks, strokes and cancer were significantly higher than the average! While power lines radiate negative energy only 20-30 yards, with transformer stations this distance may be 100 to even 400 yards!!!

Electricity is not the sole source of negative energy. There are many others, too - underground waters, radioactive radiation, cosmic radiation, etc.

As we see, there are three basic groups of negative energy:

1 Natural
2 Artificial
3 Cosmic

In Chapter 9 (Dowsing) we'll discuss each group in more detail, along with the ways to measure the negative energy and protect ourselves from it. One thing you have to remember: Nobody is immune to negative energy! There are only different ways we react to them.

The effects show after staying in a negative area for a long period of time. We might experience them in our work place, office, bedroom, and so on. The reactions depend on our sensibility. If you are sensitive to it, you will have trouble, for instance, sleeping in a negative area. You would be turning and tossing all night and wake up tired. If you are not sensitive to it, you would have greater difficulties in the years to come. If the negative source is very powerful, you would more than likely develop a serious health problem without any obvious reason!

Dowsing is the only affordable method of finding these negative areas, but until you get to that chapter, you might want to know that babies and animals are very sensitive to those areas.

Many young parents have terrible problems putting their babies to sleep. If they could only know how a baby feels in negative energy! Many times just moving them away to another room will guarantee them a peaceful sleep! I have had cases when the only positive area in the whole house was the kitchen. However, parents turn into strong believers only minutes after their baby falls into a deep sleep - on the kitchen counter!

Animals have many extra senses that are out of reach of humankind. They feel the changes in weather, travel long distances by their natural compasses, even feel the upcoming earthquakes. A same extra-sense enables them to feel negative energy. Some of them prefer it, like bees, ants, and the closest ones to us - cats! Consequently, if your cat takes its favorite naps always at the same place, you can be sure it is negative. If it is your bed-you better be concerned! On the other hand, our best friends, the dogs, will never lie down on a negative spot. Have you ever built a dog house which your dog wouldn't step in for all the bones in the world? Now you know the reason why.

THE INFLUENCE OF INJURIES

It is not a big secret how our bodies react to injuries. Cuts, broken bones, bruises, burns - they all hurt. The physiology of pain is well known to modern medical science, however, there are still millions of questions unanswered. Why do we get headaches, back pain, neck pain, etc., for no obvious reason? Why do those pains go away sometimes for no reason, or, why don't they go away, even though we try everything to get rid of them? The more questions we ask, the more complicated the answers get.

Finding the reason for back and neck problems is somewhat easier, knowing the bad postural habits of the modern human. We try to defy gravity from the time we get up until the time we go to bed. There is hardly a school in the world where students are seriously taught how to sit or walk properly. I must also mention the poor posture of virtually every office employee. Thanks to soft seats in our cars and homes, our posture is no better even outside school or work. So far, chiropractic and massage health care has been providing a pretty good help to some, but if we don't learn to keep our bodies at a ninety-degree angle to the ground, we will constantly be vulnerable. The gravity always wins!

How does energy apply here? Well, as we learned, energy is there to protect us from practically anything that would put us out of balance. When we place our muscles in an awkward, straining position, it is against the natural, established balance, not only in our body's alignment, but in the energy field, as well. To fight bad posture, the muscles will tighten up at the most offended areas. For the same reason, the energy field tends to thicken up at the corresponding areas, making the "shield" stronger for more protection to the body. Both the muscle and the energy reactions happen at the same time, which leads us to the conclusion that taking off the excess energy might actually help relieve muscle tension.

Similar reactions take place during all headaches, too. Whether the reason for a headache is stress, tight neck, digestive difficulties, or anything else, one detail is for sure: There is excess bioenergy around the head! There are no exceptions! With this knowledge even if we can't find the origin of it, we can definitely fight the pain. Just by removing the surplus energy we can stop the ache in only minutes, which is faster than a pain-pill! In my ten years of practicing biotherapy, there has been only one person I have had to work on for more then five minutes to relieve a headache. With a series of treatments, biotherapy is one of the most successful remedies for migraine headache!

As we see, each time we feel pain, regardless of the cause, there is an overabundance of bioenergy in our aura.

Sudden injuries are followed by the same type of excess energy, however, it comes as fast as the injury occurs. A broken arm, for instance, will result in a panic reaction of the energy field, sending great amounts of bioenergy to the area in need for protection. Treatment in this case is more complicated. It would be easy to take off the pain in the same manner as we do it with headaches, but then the natural healing process would be slowed down. Since the extra energy is there to heal the injury, we are not supposed to take it all off, but only to smooth it out. It will ease the pain a little bit, and at the same time there will still be enough to do the job of healing.

The same rule is valid for burns, bruises and other injuries. The only exceptions are cuts. Healing of those may be dramatically speeded up by adding bioenergy, while the pain is usually not so crucial. There have been numerous cases when bleeding was stopped in an incredible time just by holding the wound while concentrating on giving energy.

THE INFLUENCE OF EXERCISE

"In a healthy body there is a healthy mind." This old Greek saying is indeed valid for the body's energy fields, too. Regular exercise will help maintain not just the muscles', but the whole person's health as well. It is general knowledge how different types of exercise help different functions of the body. Aerobic exercise will help the cardiovascular system, the lungs, etc.; weight training will build and tone muscles.

There is suitable activity for everyone, which will more or less improve the energy circulation in the body. Besides regular workouts, there are some exercises that emphasize energy balancing over muscular enhancement. Most of them were developed thousands of years ago in the Far East. Such are Yoga, Qi Gong, and T'ai Chi. All of these are very slow in motion, with the accent on the breathing. Connecting deep breathing with special movements can lead the mind into a meditative state in which a conscious rejuvenation of bioenergy may occur.

More on the energy enhancing exercises in chapter 11.

THE INFLUENCE OF THOUGHTS

I have a theory to add to the previous sub-title: "With a healthy mind your body can always be healthy!" This is very true.

Following the British colonization of India, the world met with the amazing mind power of the masters of yoga. During demonstrations they would lie on beds made out of needles, showing no pain. Some of them were buried for days with no water, food, or even air, and survived! They showed exceptional mind control through regulating their involuntary muscles and autonomic nervous system! All of this was accomplished by years of meditative training, in reality proving that it is possible to govern the body with our thoughts.

Today, there are numerous techniques of meditation known by the general public: Creative visualization, self-hypnosis, and Jose Silva's "Mindcontrol" are but a few.

Meditation, if done correctly, is the most effective way to balance your own energy fields. Practicing it regularly will prevent your aura from misalignment, and additionally, it will definitely make you feel better through more self-confidence and self-awareness.

In chapter 11 we'll talk more about meditation, while chapter 12 will teach you long-distance healing through meditation.

If you don't practice meditation - don't worry. There are many other ways of improving your bioenergy through your thoughts. Positive thinking is one of them. It is not just being an optimist. Positive thinking is about finding, seeing, and accepting the good side of everything in your life.

If it is a dark, rainy day, think of it as a help for the vegetation. If you break an arm, it is better then breaking your neck! If someone asks you about your health, your family, or your business, try always to answer, "Better and better." This concept will influence your subconscious, and through that your energy. Every day you attend the school of life, so try to pull the good things out of it. A positive attitude will always keep you in a good mood and good health. If you are able to see a half-empty glass as half-full, you are on a good path!

On the other hand, if you are negative, your bioenergy-level will drop, too. How many times have you gotten the flu or any other disease just because someone else had it, and your mind accepted the fact that you would get it as well. That way of thinking gives the white flag to your immune system, which automatically surrenders itself to the illness.

Remember: **Your head is the general, while your body is the army on the battlefield!** Whatever you command, your body will produce. Even if those are subconscious thoughts, it will be a command! That is the reason why you should think positively all the time. Whether it gets to your subconscious or not, as long as it is positive, there will be no harm done.

How can you change your thinking to the positive? It is hard, but with practice it is achievable like everything else. First, you have to erase all the negative words from your vocabulary, at least for the time they are not necessary. No, not, bad, faulty, poor, unsatisfactory, harmful, severe, evil, problem, etc., are all words that you want to avoid. Instead, even if you have to think a little bit longer to make up a positive sentence - do it. It will be to your benefit. Exercise you mind! You will always find something positive even in the worst events!

And if someone asks you how your biotherapy practicing is going, just tell them, "Better and better!!!"

THE INFLUENCE OF FOOD

"You are what you eat"

Don't take this literally, although your diet is very important. From the energy point of view, if we follow the Chinese beliefs which claim that we obtain three different Chi's (by birth, by the air we breathe, and by the food we eat), there is indeed a close connection between our bioenergy and our diet.

There are as many theories about healthy diets as trees in the forest. Therefore, I wouldn't like to start preaching about the advantages of vegetarian or macrobiotic foods, or juicing or any other ways of nourishment. However, I would like to discuss some false beliefs in the modern nutritional habits.

-"Fresh fruit is good for you."

Well, yes it is. But 90% of the fruit that is on display in different food stores is not ripe! It looks ripe, but it is not. In order to transport fruit to distributors far away, it has to be harvested long before it is ripe, otherwise it wouldn't survive the trip. It obtains the color in storage or on the way, some even at the final destination. So, what you really eat is fruit as unripe as when it was harvested. If you ever stole some green fruit from your neighbor as a kid, you know exactly how you felt when you ate it. Your stomach hurt for a punishment. Maybe you have adjusted to it by now, but your stomach is still not happy when it gets the "green fruit" treatment. When buying fruit, always get the one that is in season, preferably in your area. If that is not possible, just try not to overeat.

With fruit and vegetables there is another existing problem: pesticides. When did you last see a worm in your apple? We used to say: "If it's good for the worm, it's good for me." The chemicals that keep the crop "healthy" and "worm-less" are impossible to wash off with regular running water. They are impossible to wash off period! Even if you peel an apple, you still haven't removed the chemicals concentrated in it. This is the case with meat and everything else we eat today! So, what can we do? I don't know. I sure hope that someday somebody will come up with a solution. Until then, be reasonable with everything you eat. "Organic farms" are a good idea, but as of now, they are still expensive and are too few to feed us all.

-"Milk is good for you."

Yes, if you are a baby sucking it. Milk is food. The only way food can be digested completely is if the digestion starts in the mouth, that is: mixed with saliva. Consequently, if you drink milk in large quantities from a cup, it doesn't have the ability to mix with the first digestive fluid, and enters the stomach "unprepared". Besides getting an upset stomach, your body can not use the majority of the nutrients found in milk. So, if you are not a baby, try to drink your milk through a straw, or in small sips.

While talking about milk, we have to mention pasteurization and homogenization. These processes that are necessary for preservation also destroy a lot of enzymes that are essential for healthy digestion. A study in Scotland a while ago tested the difference between raw and pasteurized milk by feeding eight calves with one, and eight calves with the other. The first group was developing healthy and normally, while the second group, fed by pasteurized milk, developed difficulties. After six weeks, six calves in the second group died. The remaining two were saved only by giving them "raw" milk.

-"Fish is good for you."

Definitely! I love fish! However, the once considered healthy food has become hazardous in many areas. The pollution all around the world teaches us lessons in seafood consumption. Stories about poisons in shellfish, especially raw oysters are not new anymore. Raw shrimp may be diseased by salmonella or other type of bacteria. <u>Any</u> raw fish may be contaminated by bacteria or parasites. Mahimahi, tuna, and mostly swordfish often have high levels of mercury. Unfortunately the list doesn't stop here. The good news is that there is still some healthy seafood out there. Salmon, flounder, sole, and all the farm raised fish are considered pollutant-free, and nutritious. Preparation of fish is also very important. It has to be cooked as soon as possible, or has to be frozen. Fish is highly perishable and a favorite playground for bacteria.

The above examples are not supposed to scare you, but to encourage you to seek the right diet. So much about diets has been written, that it is difficult to find the right one. Which one you choose is up to you. If you are undecided, you might find help in dowsing, in chapter 9.

If you wish to find out more about pollutants, parasites, bacteria and all the other health hazards of modern living, I suggest you to read <u>The Cure for All Diseases</u> by Hulda Regehr Clark, Ph.D., N.D., published by ProMotion Publishing.

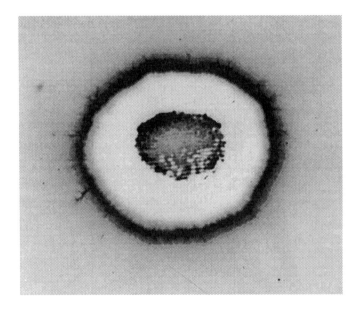

THE TECHNIQUE AND THE MOVEMENTS OF BIOTHERAPY

For centuries touch-less healing, or healing by laying on of hands, was the privilege of kings, emperors, priests and other "gifted" people. We learned in a previous chapter that you don't have to be "special" to see or to feel the aura. Consequently, you don't have to be special to manipulate it, either. If your and other people's auras are already palpable for you, it is easy to learn how to use that knowledge for the benefit of you, your family, friends, and others.

In this chapter you will learn the common movements of energy manipulation in biotherapy.

There are three major groups of manipulations of the energy fields of the body:

1) Spreading out the aura
2) Taking energy
3) Giving energy

These three types of movements are further divided into many sub-categories that we are going to discuss.

Depending on the nature of the problem, in most of the treatments you will use the combination of at least two types of movements.

1. SPREADING OUT THE AURA

It is very important to even out the aura before the start of the treatment. That will give you a good base for the examination of the energy field, which takes place at the beginning of every session.

It is preferred to have your "patient"[1] in standing position, because it gives you access to the whole body without any obstructions and difficulties. However, a treatment can be done with the same success whether the person is standing, sitting or lying down.

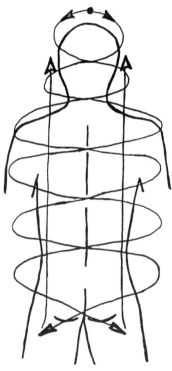

Put your right hand (or left if you are left handed) over your patient's head, approximately 2 inches from the top. Keep it there for about ten seconds, or as long as you need to establish contact. Your next move is to join both hands at the top of the head, which is followed by circular, "crossing" movements all the way down to the base of the trunk. Then, from the bottom of the trunk, continue to move your hands straight up to shoulder level.

As you go down, the palms of your hands should face the body, while as you go up, let your hands

---

[1]Patient is not the most appropriate word. We might also use "client", "subject" or simply "person". I hope not to offend anyone.

and fingers relax, and face the body with the back of your hands.

You can do the movements of spreading (or "opening" the aura) more than once, just remember to always start in front of the body, and only when you are finished with it, continue with the back of the body, doing the same procedure. There are some exceptions when only the back is done, but for practice, it is best if you do the whole process.

Note: The number of the "crossings" is not important (it is usually about 7 - depending on the height of the person on whom you are working). Also, you don't have to concentrate on, or cross in front of the chakras. Remember, it is the whole aura you are working on!

2. TAKING THE ENERGY

We take off bioenergy from parts of the aura either in order to relieve pain, or just to "clean" the area before giving "fresh" energy. It is a very easy and effective procedure, that in some cases, gives amazing results. For instance, by taking off the excess bioenergy around the head, we can stop a headache in only minutes!

During the energy taking process, your patient may feel some coldness or chill to the body-part near the site of the aura manipulation.

There are two basic ways of taking the energy from a body-part:

-Pulling the energy away from the excess-energy area by following the contours of the body, or

-Pulling the energy straight out of the aura in a ninety degree angle

If choosing the first procedure, there is one general rule to remember: <u>When taking off the bioenergy, always go from medial to lateral, and from superior to inferior.</u>

This means that you should move the excess energy from the midline, or the trunk of the body towards the sides (or the limbs), and from the top of the head towards the bottom of the feet. If you are working on the arms or the legs, take off the energy towards the fingers or the toes.

A. The "**Sweeping Movements**" are usually done around the whole body, however, they are very practical for reducing pain in local areas. These movements are the easiest to perform, and even beginners are able to get serious results through them in a short period of time.

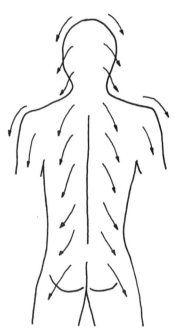

A1. To reduce the bioenergy around the whole body (to weaken the aura), start from the top of the head. Keep the palms of your hands at the established distance of about 2-3 inches from the body, and make sweeping movements, in the way you would sweep off snow from someone's coat. Gradually, move your hands from the top of the head towards the bottom of the trunk, doing the same light motions. If your patient is lying down, you may continue all the way to the bottom of the feet. The length of the sweeps themselves is about 10-12 inches.

You may repeat the movements from the top to the bottom several times, depending on your own perceptions and judgement.

This type of manipulation is a common part of the art of Therapeutic Touch.

A2. Another way of sweeping off the energy is one continuous move instead of many small movements. They follow the same direction, but this time the hands don't stop till they reach the bottom of the trunk or the bottom of the feet. The effect is the same and it saves time, but you have to be more experienced in order to be successful.

This movement can be very effective in reducing high blood pressure if done from the top of the shoulders to the base of the spine.

When working on local areas as the head or the limbs, this might be the only procedure required to relieve pain.

When working on the head, start the sweeping movements from the top of the head and follow a route down the sides

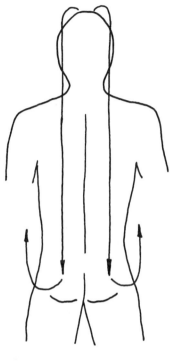

towards the shoulders. Then, make a wide circle with your hands to return to the top. The second time follow a route down the back of the head and neck, to the middle of the thoracic area, or if you are facing the person, go in front of the face to

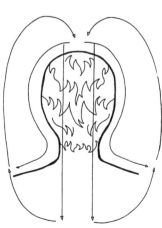

the middle of the chest. Your hands should go up to the top of the head the same way, in a wide circle away from the body. Continue the movements several times, alternately changing the route in order to cover the whole area around the head.

When working on the arms, start from the top of the shoulders while standing at the side of the person. Follow a route passing the

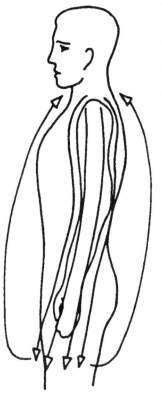

upper arm, elbows, forearm, wrist and fingers, making sure to finish the movement a little bit further from the tips of the fingers (approximately 6-7"). Again, go back to the shoulders in a wide

circle. This route can also be done both ways: short, repeated sweeping, or one long movement.

The same rules are effective for working on the legs and feet. Always start from the top (in this case the hip) and go towards the feet. The movements always end further away from the toes.

B. The **"Pulling Movements"** are done by taking the energy away from the body in a ninety degree angle. This time it is not sweeping off the bioenergy, but more like grasping or grabbing it and taking it out of the aura. The main rule to remember here is to always get rid of the excess energy in order to protect yourself during the treatments. Doing that is very easy: just shake your hands at the end of every pulling movement in the way you would shake your tight gloves off. Also, any time you feel a slight pain in your hands you can do the same procedure, because it usually means that you have some excess energy left around your hands. Excess energy may also be removed by putting your hands under running water for a few minutes, but if you follow the rules it will not be necessary. [2]

B1. This is a very powerful energy taking-movement if it is done the correct way. To make it easy, use your imagination: Try to visualize the energy field as a kind of a fluid around the body.

Hold your hands straight out towards the body-part needing attention, and keep them there for a few seconds to establish good contact with the aura. You can also make slow vibration-like movements with your fingers, which will help you pick up more bioenergy. Follow this with a grasping (or better, "clawing" -because you don't close your hands all the way) movement done by both hands and pull the energy (or 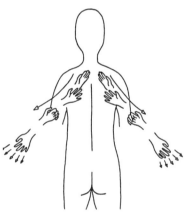 the imagined fluid) out of the aura. During this motion, your hands will move past your trunk, ending up behind you. There, make a short, shaking movement to get rid of the energy you have just taken off. Resume the movements as long as you

---

[2] Water is strongly energy-absorbent. It can easily be energized, but it also drains your energy if you are submerged in it for a while. Just remember how tired you are after a long bath.

think is necessary and check the energy field with your palms after you are finished.

All of the energy-taking movements may be repeated if the result is not satisfactory, as many times as you want, except when the pain is relieved - you can stop right away.

B2. A similar energy-taking movement may be done by only one hand, except this time enclose the energy in your hands by closing your fingertips together, making a bird's beak shape. The path is the same, too: After grasping the excess energy, pull it out of the aura and take it all the way behind you to shake it off.

You may do the same movement with your hand turned upside down, however, that way don't close your hands all the way.

C. With the "**Circular Movements**" we also take the energy away in a ninety degree angle. It is a good energy-taking movement for small, local areas. A rule to remember while taking off the energy by this motion is to always go counter-clockwise (to give energy is the opposite).

Hold your hand for a few seconds over the body part to be treated, to establish contact. Now, slowly start making small, circular, counter-clockwise motions. As you go further away

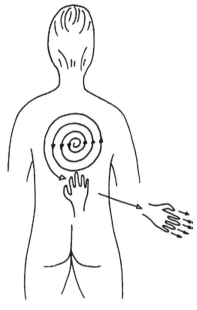

from the body, gradually make the circles larger and larger (so you get a funnel-like picture) until you reach a distance from the body of approximately one foot. Then, get a hold of the separated energy by your established grasping motion, and pull it out of the aura. Finish the movement by shaking off the excess energy.

D. The **"Salting Movements"** are in a way also circular movements, however, in this case, the fingers are our main instruments. The salting movements are used for very small local areas, like for instance, the ears.

Start again by establishing contact with your patients aura. Slowly, put your fingers together in a way you would hold salt, with your fingertips pointing towards the treated area. As you move your hand away, simultaneously make salting motions with your fingers (what is basically just softly rubbing the fingertips together). If you are already experienced in seeing the aura, you might see a thin blurry line between your fingertips and the treated area during this procedure. Finish again by shaking off the taken energy.

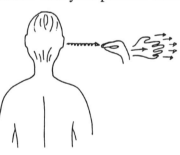

3. GIVING ENERGY

Energy-giving is the primary healing movement in biotherapy. This is what the whole therapy is about! To restore the healthy balance in the body's energy field, we need to fill up the energy-deficient areas with fresh bioenergy.

There are two basic ways of giving energy to a body-part:

-Pulling the bioenergy from the surrounding areas towards the energy-lacking area, or

-Directly giving off the energy from ourselves

If selecting the first procedure, the main rule to remember is: When giving bioenergy, always go from lateral to medial, and from inferior to superior.

This means that you always have to go from the sides (or the limbs) towards the trunk of the body, and from the bottom of the trunk (or of the feet) towards the head.

During the energy-giving procedure, both the therapist and the patient may feel some warmth, tingling, or pressure. In some cases, the heat may be so intense, it will cause a sweat! This is also one of the unexplainable effects of energy-giving. According to Newtonian physics, when we merge a hot and a cold object, the hot object will give off heat to the cold object, until their temperatures equalize. If we suppose that those objects could sense temperature, than the cold object would feel the heat, while the hot object would feel coolness during the temperature exchange. However, during energy-giving in a biotherapy session both the therapist and the subject usually feel intense heat! This sensation in not new. It is also present between lovers during their tender moments.

A. The "**Drawing Movements**" are the easiest to perform of all the energy-giving movements, as long as you go by the above described rules. They are the exact opposite of the energy-taking sweeping movements.

A1. To give bioenergy to the whole body, always start your movements from the bottom of the feet, or the bottom of the

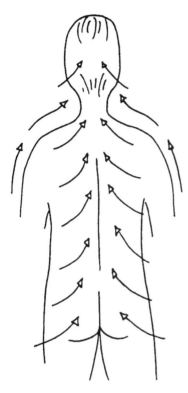

trunk, depending on the position of your patient. Horizontal position saves the therapist's back, but if there is no need for work on the legs, choose the standing position for better access.

Your hands may be turned either in or out - whichever is more comfortable. Keep the established 2-3 inch distance from the body, and slowly bring up the energy from your starting position in small, approximately

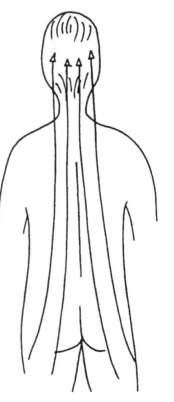

one foot steps. After every step go back a few inches and do another one, continuing so, until you reach the top of the head. You may repeat these movements as many times as you want, both on the back and/or the front of the body, always following a different path to cover every spot.

A2. Just like the sweeping movements, the drawing movements can also be executed in one long step. Do

the whole procedure as described above, but without stopping.

To return to the starting position, this time, you don't have to go around the aura. Instead, as you go down, gently stroke the energy-field with the palms of your hands, at about a 6 inch distance from the body.

If done several times from the base of the spine to the top of the shoulders, this movement can be very effective in the treatment of low blood pressure.

Individual body-parts are treated the same way, starting at the fingers and ending at the shoulders for the arms, and starting at the toes and ending at the hips for the legs.

B. The "**Pushing Movements**" look exactly like the energy- awareness exercise we have done before.

Put your hands in a parallel position, with your palms facing each other. The distance between your hands should be about one foot. This is an energy-giving movement for local areas, so direct your fingertips towards the area to be treated. After establishing contact, start moving your

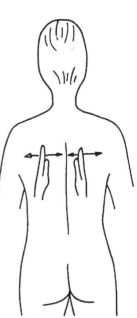

hands towards each other in a way you would clap, but stop when you reach about an inch distance. You can imagine having some elastic, squeezable material between your palms, because that is precisely what you are going to perceive. After reaching the end of the movement, go back to the starting position, and resume with the same motions in a rhythmic manner for as long as you think is necessary.

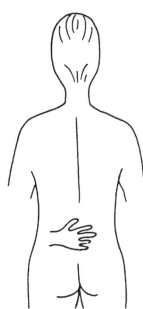

C. "**Holding The Hand**" on, or over the treated area is the most common energy-giving technique. It is also known as healing by laying on of hands. It is done very easily: Just hold your hand over the energy-deficient area and concentrate on giving off your bioenergy to it. You can also lay your hand on the body, however, that system is not so effective because you can't feel the aura if the sensation of touch interferes.

If appropriate, you may use both hands,

placing them on the opposite sides of the body, making an "energy-connection" between them. This type of energy-giving is usually followed with a sensation of intense heat.

The Holding The Hand technique, while the subject is standing or sitting, may also be performed with your hand in a horizontal position with the thumb

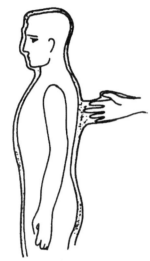

turned either up or to the side. In that case the emphasis is on "**Directing The Energy**" to an <u>exact</u> location - which you should be aware of.

This movement (with the thumbs up) is also effective in giving energy to the spine, as long as you move your hand vertically from the coccyx to the cervical region and back.

D. The energy-giving "**Circular Movements**" are almost the exact opposite of the energy-taking circular movements. The rule to remember is simple: When giving energy using this method, always go clockwise!

Start by establishing contact with the aura (I suppose you have become used to this by now) over the area to be treated.

If you know the precise location of the energy-deficient spot, begin circling the palm of your hand around it. The circles may differ in diameter, depending on the problem. It is all up to you! If you don't know the exact location - don't worry. While you circle around the area, you will feel the increase in temperature, which will lead you to the exact spot.

The speed of circling should be about one per second, depending on the diameter of the circles. The distance between the hand and the body is also up to you, depending on the size of the energy-deficient area. The smaller the size, the closer you may go.

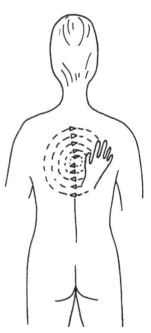

In circular movements you may also use both hands. Place them on the opposite sides of the body and follow your routine.

This movement is very effective in every aspect of energy-giving, however, it is used mainly in restoring the healthy, funnel shape of the chakras.

Both the "Holding The Hand" and the "Circular Movements" may be done together with "**Hand Vibration**". It is believed that vibrating the fingers and the hands in a combined speed of approximately 8-12 cycles per second (Hz), speeds up the energy-transfer between the therapist and the client. I have been using this technique for a long time, but I have never had the chance to actually measure the speed of the vibrations. Regardless, it works for me, so give it a try - it might work for you, too.

E. The "**Horizontal Crossing Movements**" are primarily used over the shoulders and knees, as well as below the shoulder line in the middle of the front and behind the body to give energy to the lungs.

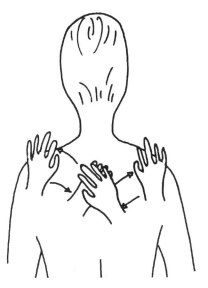

Start by crossing your hands in front of your chest, approximately 1-2 feet from your patient, with your palms facing him/her. To give energy this way, you have to open your hands in a natural manner, using only a movement that comes from your elbows. That will lead your hands from the crossed position to a wide angle. If working on the lungs, your hands will end up a little bit wider then the shoulder line. To work on the knees or the shoulders, it is not necessary to go so wide. It is all up to your judgement.

There will be a lot of heat and pressure during this maneuver!

F. "**Connecting**" is a procedure which enables us to force the flow of bioenergy between two points. It may be executed in two different ways:

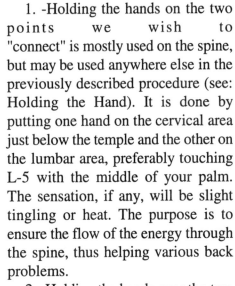

1. -Holding the hands on the two points we wish to "connect" is mostly used on the spine, but may be used anywhere else in the previously described procedure (see: Holding the Hand). It is done by putting one hand on the cervical area just below the temple and the other on the lumbar area, preferably touching L-5 with the middle of your palm. The sensation, if any, will be slight tingling or heat. The purpose is to ensure the flow of the energy through the spine, thus helping various back problems.

2. -Holding the hands over the two points you wish to connect is followed by more sensation on both sides. It may be done over any part of the body, but usually preferred for work on extremities. The feeling during this movement is virtually amazing. If you do it right, you'll definitely question some of the laws of physics!

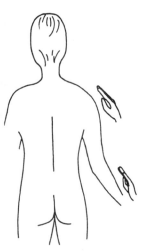

Before you start, it is interesting to get the "energy-ball" between your hands, by placing your hands opposite each other. Play with it for a while to make sure you have it. Only now, put your hands over the points you wish to connect and continue "playing" with the ball. Even if your hands are not opposing each other, you will still feel the ball! Every little movement you make will be perceived as the ball was there: pleasant heat, some tingling, and an intense feeling of magnetic resistance.

All the described movements are from personal experience, and most of them are used by many other biotherapists. If you feel you have discovered a new one, don't hesitate to use it.

Practice and enjoy!

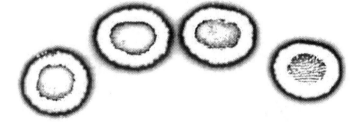

The General Rules of Biotherapy

Before you start any treatments there are some details you should keep in mind.

- A biotherapist is not a doctor! Only a physician is authorized to make diagnoses, suggest, and practice the treatment. Traditional and modern medicine should work together. Don't try to influence your "patient" in fields that are unfamiliar to you. Base your treatment both on the official diagnoses and your own findings. Remember, you are working only on the energy fields of the body! You can not prescribe any medicine, however, you may suggest some energy-enhancing exercises, meditation, or eventually self-massage, reflexology, and better dietary habits, all in all, a change towards a healthy lifestyle.

- To be able to treat others, you must be in a perfect health. If you are ill, your bioenergy-field is not in an ideal balance, and you may do more harm than good - whether to others or to yourself!

- Read the book a few times and do a lot of practice before you engage in an actual healing. You have to be entirely familiar with your own abilities before you start. If for the reason of not knowing the right procedure, you give energy instead of taking it off, you might cause a lot of discomfort or pain! Also, by taking off more energy than required, you may harm rather than help. So, be careful!

- Don't do too many treatments in a day until getting in good shape for it. Try not to drain your own energy! It takes time, just like your muscles need more workout before actually using their total capacity.

- Sometimes one is enough, however, most of the times you'll need to do a series of treatments on each individual. Occasionally, months will pass before reaching the final goal. If that is the case, make sure to pause for a week after a two-week treatment.

In the next chapter you'll get the idea of what a series of treatments looks like, and when is the best time to start and finish.

- Biotherapy is not a magical, everything-fixing medicine. Although you should always think positively, try to be realistic. Don't give anyone false hopes. If you are not sure of the outcome, just say that you will try your best.

- If you work on someone who is prone to fainting, I suggest a lying or sitting position for the treatment.

- Treatments may be done at any time of the day as long as you are not exhausted or tired. Take a break, don't push yourself too hard!

- To get good results, you have to love what you do! Treat every individual as one of your own family. If you are able to feel other people's pain and suffering as your own - you will be a great healer! Remember: **The strongest healing power in the world is the power of love!!!**

The Profile of the Treatments

As mentioned before, make sure that you are physically and mentally relaxed before starting any energy-balancing work.

You can do biotherapy treatments anywhere and anytime, however, naturally it is better if you have previously prepared a comfortable, pleasant environment. Soothing music, dimmed lights, green plants, etc., will all help to create a relaxing atmosphere.

To avoid being misconstrued as a "psychic", always explain what you are doing. This is not some mystic ritual, but indeed a very scientific approach to energy-healing.

Before you start, get familiar with the people you are going to treat. Ask them about their background and their major problems. When you master biotherapy, you may skip this part, so you can impress them by finding the problem areas yourself.

The treatment itself is most effective if done with the subject in a standing position, because that way you can easily go around the aura without any obstruction. However, if it is not applicable because of your subject's situation or the length of the treatment, you may chose sitting or lying down position.

The pattern is usually the same: It begins with **"opening the aura"** and **assessment**, followed by **taking off the excess energy**, then **giving energy**, and finally **closing the aura and assessment.**

As mentioned before, start by establishing contact with your patient's aura, which is done by holding your hand over the top of the head for about ten seconds, or as needed. Continue by opening the aura, using the "spreading" movements, both on the front and the back of the body. Now comes the most important part: assessment.

Assessment or evaluation is the segment of biotherapy that needs all of your concentration. During this procedure you have to find the areas in the aura that are out of balance.

Go around the whole body, touching the aura with the palms of your hands (or the one hand that is more sensitive) and register all the areas where you feel some imbalances. Don't hesitate to ask your patients for feedback. They might feel some differences in their energy fields, too. As you already know, the reactions may be heat, tingling, pressure, as well as cold or any other sensation.

The distance from your palms to the body should be about 3", however it varies from one to another. You might feel the aura better from closer or farther away than that. Also, as you know, there are more layers of the aura, so you may examine it from much farther than 3", as long as you can do so effectively.

After you have determined where the problem areas are, you may proceed with putting them back in balance by giving or taking off energy. Start with taking off the excess energy, which will usually give an instant relief to the painful areas. Choose one or more of the already established methods - whichever is more suitable for the certain situation. You may also take off some energy from the whole aura to make it more susceptible to the bioenergy you are getting ready to give. Some experts even suggest taking some energy off the whole aura every time, this way "cleaning" it of the "dirty" or "polluted" energy.[1]

---

[1]Don't forget to shake off the excess energy from your hands! You may also use a different method to protect yourself. One is to hold your hands for a while under running water, which also takes the bioenergy away. However, there are

After finishing with each area, make sure you have achieved the desired results. This may be done by assessing the aura, or simply by asking your patient for feedback.

The next step is to give energy to the deficient parts of the aura (or the whole aura in case you have taken energy from it). Again, you have a whole variety of methods at your disposal to complete this task.

Finish by assessing and closing the aura. You may close the aura using the same method as for opening it.

There is a controversial way of ending the treatment, which includes tapping the upper back of the patient (upper trapezius area close to the neck) with the forefingers, causing a mild shock reaction. According to the theory, every function of the body is controlled by a certain "clock". That means that we have millions and millions of timepieces scattered throughout our organs. If our energy fields are out of balance, these clocks are not synchronized. Some of them are too fast, while some are too slow to maintain their regular function.

During a biotherapy session, a great majority of people become very relaxed and mellow. Now, if we give them a small shock at the end of the session by tapping the upper trapezius muscles, all the clocks in the body will stop simultaneously for a split second, which will synchronize them, so they will start working together!

Note: It is not necessary to hit exactly the trapezius, but it is convenient, because the finishing "crossing" movements end up exactly at the shoulders.

While mentioning the internal "clock" we should take a look at the best timing for biotherapy sessions, too.

---

ways to defend yourself even during the treatment by putting up a "mental block" or "wall". More about this in the chapter about energy enhancing exercises.

From very young age we have followed certain "rules" that are connected to time. We have been taught when to eat breakfast, lunch, dinner, when to go to bed, when to get up, etc. There is also a very important rhythm engraved in our subconscious mind: the days of the week. If you really think about it, it will make sense. Day care, school, work...everything for most of us starts on Monday and ends on Friday, eventually Saturday. Sunday is generally a day off. Our bodies and minds get used to it. Even though you can take a good rest on Sundays, Mondays feel like a torture. It is like waking up in the morning trying to start the "engine". At the same time, Fridays are "almost week-end", and you are ready for the last push of the week. So, the peak of your performance is usually around Wednesday or Thursday. Consequently, it is easy to compare the days of the week to the hours of the day. This correlation can be very useful in timing the biotherapy sessions when multiple treatments are needed.

Experience shows that the best day for the first treatment is Monday. You may compare it to sunrise. The energy of the

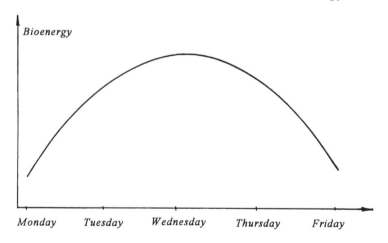

biotherapist is on "low", as is the energy of the patient. There is almost no possibility of "overcharging" the aura and giving an energy shock to the body, especially at the very first treatment. As mentioned before, some people might be more sensitive to the treatment, causing dizziness or lightheadedness. The first session should be relatively mild, with the emphasis on assessment.

If possible, continue the treatments every day until Friday, following the sunrise-sunset system. The energy and the effects will be the strongest at the middle of the week, while they will slowly calm down by Friday and Saturday.

Studies and personal practice have shown that the best results are accomplished if treatments are done in a five-day series. If a very long therapy is needed, after a five day/two week series, take a one week break. This time is necessary for the patient's energy field to get used to the changes. When final results are achieved, have another session about a month later for a final assessment and treatment, which will put an end to the therapy.

There is another internal clock worth mentioning, although because of its wide range, the possibility of utilizing it in biotherapy is minimal. It is the internal timing of the "high-tide" of the qi.

According to the theory of acupuncture, there is a 24 hour cycle of the energy traveling through the body, following certain routes. These passages are the twelve major meridians. The sum of all the energy that circulates in them is called "Jing Qi".

Every meridian is coupled with one of the main organs or body functions, that way feeding the corresponding area with energy. Each day there is a peak time when the energy is the strongest at individual body parts. This period is called the "energy high-tide". As there are 24 hours in a day, it is easy to figure out that the qi travels through every meridian in exactly two hours.

The meridians are also connected to the five "basic elements", which are, according to the Chinese philosophy, the correlations of all the occurrences in the universe, or in people -

the relationship of the organs. Every element has two meridians. As everything else, the meridians are also divided to Yin and Yang. The following chart presents the correlation of the five elements, the organs and the time of the high-tide of the energy.

ELEMENT	MERIDIAN	ORGAN	TIME
Metal	Shou Tai Yin	Lungs	3-5 AM
	Shou Yang Ming	Large Intestines	5-7 AM
Earth	Zu Yang Ming	Stomach	7-9 AM
	Zu Tai Yin	Spleen	9-11 AM
Fire (Imperial)	Shou Shao Yin	Heart	11 AM-1 PM
	Shou Tai Yang	Small Intestines	1-3 PM
Water	Zu Tai Yang	Bladder	3-5 PM
	Zu Shao Yin	Kidney	5-7 PM
Fire (Ministerial)	Shou Jue Yin	Pericardium	7-9 PM
	Shou Shao Yang	Triple Warmer	9-11 PM
Wood	Zu Shao Yang	Gall-Bladder	11 PM-1 AM
	Zu Jue Yin	Liver	1-3 AM

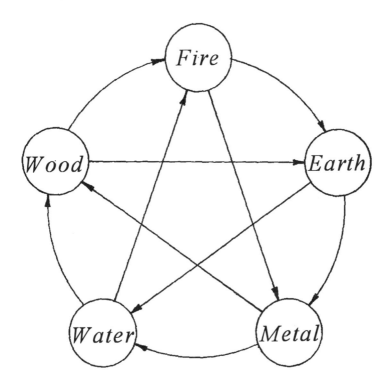

As we see, it would be very hard to apply the timing of the high-tide of the energy into our biotherapy sessions. Nevertheless, this knowledge is helpful to understand the "programming" of the ever-renewing vital processes of the body.

EVALUATING THE RESULTS

So far, for the evaluation of the results of the treatment, we have had to rely on our "feeling" of the energy field, as well as on the obvious improvement and the feedback of our patients.

However, there is a more precise way of measuring the energy fields using our "internal instruments". As with the internal clocks and the bioenergy, we are also equipped with a certain "sixth sense", too. Of course, most of us were not taught how to use that ability. The question is: How can we do an accurate measurement of the energy field with something that we are not even sure we have? Well, we all **do** have it, and we can all learn how to utilize it! The method that can turn all of us into living instruments is called: **Dowsing**.

DOWSING[1]

I don't know anyone who hasn't heard at least one story about dowsers. You know - people who look for underground water or oil wells, or even missing persons. They have been among us for centuries. Believed to have extraordinary abilities, these people have mostly been known for accurately finding underground water. There is no evidence for how long dowsing has existed, but it is believed that this knowledge has been around for thousands of years. As many ancient civilizations have left us some accounts, let's just mention the most prominent one. It is not the perfect example, but it sounds really good: Moses taps the stone with his stick, and there comes the water!

Nevertheless, there is much more evidence for dowsing in history. While Western civilizations started seriously researching this science only recently, the Chinese have known about it for over four thousand years! There are still very few houses or temples or any other buildings in China that are built without first consulting a "professional". Everything is considered: the location, negative sources, the environment, moreover, the positioning of the furniture, plants, art pieces, and mirrors in the house itself! You can say that the professional dowser in China is also your interior decorator. This very complex science is called "Feng Shui" and is taken so

---

[1]Dowsing is also called Divining or Radiesthesia, while it is very closely associated with Radionics and Psychotronics.

seriously that even large corporations consult a professional about anything from constructing an office building to the seating arrangements at a business meeting!

Well known or not, more and more people in the USA are getting involved with Feng Shui, and you'll see why.

If you: can't sleep for no obvious reason, wake up tired, feel uncomfortable in some areas of your home, can't sit long on some furniture, get tired easily in your office, can't pay attention in certain rooms, or have other discomforts, you will definitely benefit from dowsing!

As mentioned in Chapter 5, there are many different sources of either positive or negative energy in our environment. They may greatly influence our health and way of living even without our knowledge about them.

By a zone of positive energy I don't mean an area charged with (+) polarity, but a place where all the qualities for a healthy living are ideal. It might be anywhere, from a location in your house, to a site in the nearby park. As long as it is beneficial for your health, it will be a "good" spot.

Negative energy, however, is much more complex. Staying in negative areas will be more or less harmful for any individual. The intensity and its influence on us depends on many factors. To prevent ourselves from this invisible health hazard, we have to learn how to recognize it and eventually dominate it. Again, by negative energy we don't mean the polarity, but the influence on our health.

First, let's review the three basic groups of negative energy. They are:
1 Natural
2 Artificial
3 Cosmic

NATURAL SOURCES OF NEGATIVE ENERGY

Natural sources are the ones that exist spontaneously as a part of the biosphere. The energy might be emitted either by some underground water's friction with the soil, or minerals, cavities, caves, oil, etc. A common term for these negative areas is **Geopathic Zones.** Some people knew about these areas a long time ago, even outside the Orient. Moreover, they have had their own methods of protection against them. In some districts of Europe people would also check the spot before building a house, using a very unique method. The ground would be cleared of grass, and a mirror would be placed on it upside down, covered by a board. If the mirror turned dewy in the morning, it meant the place wasn't good for human occupancy.

Natural sources of negative energy are everywhere, however we should be concerned only about the ones that are at the areas where we spend most of our time. Bedrooms, work areas, offices, classrooms, living rooms, are good examples of these.

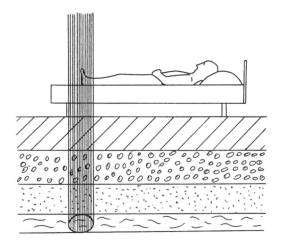

Underground water causing foot pain

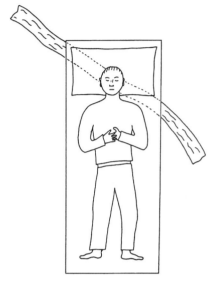

Underground water affecting the head

As a student at the university, I discovered that sitting at certain desks in different classrooms and auditoriums influenced my alertness in various ways. After a while I marked all the seats where I measured some negative energy, and from then on tried to avoid sitting in them. I even had to argue with some of my professors because of the place-switching, but the results on my tests and my higher energy level would eventually prove that my theory was right. Furthermore, as my mom was a school teacher, I made her aware too, of the negative areas in her classroom, so she could seat her "kids" away from those. Needless to mention, it resulted in more attentive and less aggressive children.

ARTIFICIAL SOURCES OF NEGATIVE ENERGY

This group indeed consists of all the sources of electromagnetic and nuclear energy. It is not a big secret how these types of energy affect living beings. In our modern, industrial, high-tech civilization there is hardly anyone who doesn't enjoy the benefits of electricity. The whole world is webbed into millions of miles of electric cables, carrying this essential energy to even the most remote areas of the planet.

However, as much as it is essential, every source of electricity is also a source of radiation of various amounts of electromagnetic fields in the surroundings. These fields are relatively harmful to all the living beings in their vicinity, depending on the voltage. The higher the voltage the more bioenergy is "drained" from the living organism.

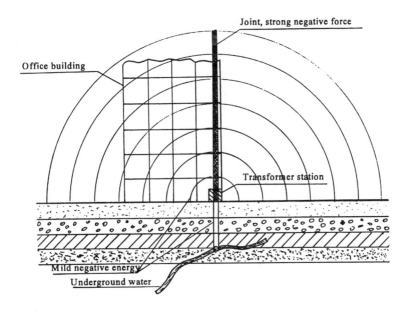

As mentioned earlier, all living cells have an electromagnetic nature that we call bioenergy. Bioenergy is almost like electricity, with very similar characteristics, therefore it is vulnerable to the effects of electricity.

How does it influence us? The same way Geopathic Zones do. Spending too much time in the locality of such forces will eventually weaken our energy fields, causing an unnatural imbalance, which leads to physical, mental or spiritual disturbances.

Protection against artificial sources of negative energy is virtually impossible, although the very strong sources (such as high-voltage electric cables, power stations, nuclear power-plants, nuclear lightning-rods, etc.) are usually far from our areas of living. However, there are still hundreds of household and office apparatuses just a reach from us. TVs, microwave ovens, computers, electro-motors, etc., are all parts of our lives. The latest craze is the cellular phones, although I haven't heard any proof yet of their highly debated brain-tumor causing effects.

As long as we are talking about artificial sources of negative energy, we shouldn't miss the effects of the human psyche. It may in fact be a very strong negative force enabled to do great destructions in bioenergy fields. So called "black magic", "spells" or "curses" are not merely science fiction or legend. The negative effect of some of our thoughts is unfortunately part of our lives. To prove this, I suggest a simple experiment:

Take two plants that are the same size and species and put them several feet from each other. Make sure to provide them the same amount of water and sunshine. Every day take a short time to "talk" to your plants (you don't actually have to make sound, it is enough if you think really hard.) Now, while you "say" all the nice things to one of them (for instance: Hi honey, you are beautiful, sweet, I love you, etc.), take all your anger and frustration out on the other one. Be very aggressive and negative to this one, and you'll see the results in a matter of days or weeks, depending on the specimen. The plant that received your positive thoughts will grow to be beautiful and healthy, while the one that you were "cursing" will stay small, dry out, and maybe even die!

This experiment also proves the connection of the mind and bioenergy, ensuring that for a good health, positive thinking is necessary! We are indeed able to harm others through negative thoughts, whether we call them black magic or not, however that means we think negatively and at the same time we also harm ourselves. Be careful and think before you act! I'm sure you have been in situations when you wanted something bad to happen to someone. But, how did you feel when it really happened?

COSMIC SOURCES OF NEGATIVE ENERGY

Our planet has been bombarded by all kinds of cosmic rays since the beginning of time. It is such a common phenomenon that its impact cannot be felt by people, animals or plants. However, it can also be divided into two basic groups: positive and negative.

Negative cosmic rays are more our concern, so let's see the most well-known examples.

By cosmic rays, we mean the free electricity that circulates in the cosmos and is radiated or received by many planets in our and other solar systems and galaxies.

Some surveys around the world have shown that cosmic rays have the ability to penetrate up to 450 meters (1350 feet) into the earth and about 600 meters (1800 feet) into water.

If this type of radiation hits hard ground (for instance, clay), it will bounce back to the atmosphere. However, on the way back to the surface, it will pick up the radiation emitted by the earth and become polluted! The daytime activity of cosmic rays is

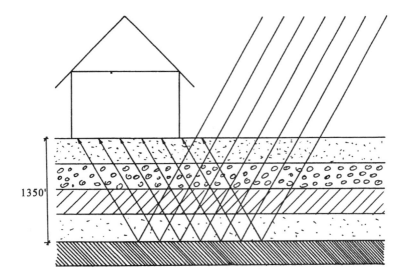

about 70% stronger than at night. The earth also has the ability to charge up with these rays and release them later (usually at night). All of this happens in everyday cycles, and there are no rules to determine in which ways cosmic rays influence our health. It mainly depends on the geological situation and our own vitality.

According to some studies, there are over twenty five different rays hitting us from outer space. However, there are only two that are really of our interest. Those are the Hartmann-, and Kerry-nets.

Dr. Ernest Hartmann developed a theory called Hartmann's net, in which the cosmic rays hit the earth in a web-like fashion. The net covers the whole planet, like latitudes and longitudes made of radiation zones (or lines) that are 20 centimeters (8") wide. This forms individual rectangles measuring 2.5 by 2 meters (8'4"x 6'8"), in an east-west direction. The whole net by itself is not dangerous except the crossings of the radiation zones which are called Hartmann's knots. The radiation zones may become harmful if they coincide with some geopathic zones.

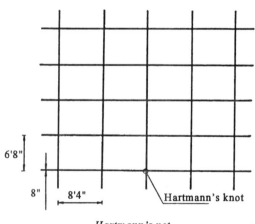

Hartmann's net

Kerry's net of harmful cosmic rays also webs the whole planet, but in north-west/south-east and south-west/north-east direction. The width of the lines is about 50 centimeters (20"), while the

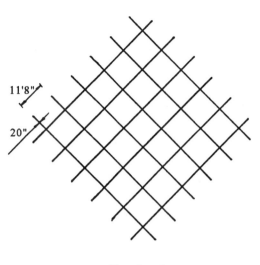

11'8"

20"

Kerry's net

distance between them is 3.5 meters (11'8").

All research in the field of harmful rays shows that there may be physiological changes in the human body triggered by these rays which could lead to ailments

A group of scientists led by Dr. Hartmann conducted experiments in this field in 1962. By the help of a "georhythmogram" they measured the influence of the terrain, weather and surroundings on the human body.

Nevertheless, even today, there is no hard evidence of the harmful effects of the cosmic rays to humans. All we know is based on statistical evidence.

As we see, we are surrounded by all kinds of negative sources. Moreover, if some, or all of these sources coincide in one area, there would hardly be any chances for healthy living. Therefore, houses where this happens, are called "death houses" by some dowsers.

PROTECTION FROM NEGATIVE ENERGY

There have been many attempts to create a reliable device for protection from negative energy, but as of today I haven't heard of any ultimate successes.

Some dowsers swear by the effect of mirrors placed upside-down under your bed, while others suggest using canned fish! Apparently, oil is able to receive all the geopathic energy, so it is advised to place about 10 unopened cans of fish in oil under your bed, which would then be protected for about a month. After use they should be put outside to get rid of the pollution and may then be reused. If you don't like fish cans, motor oil will work as well!

You may also use metal bars, which deflect negative energy, or lead plates, which receive them - like oil, or even copper cables. A glass of water placed in front of your TV screen is said to be helpful in protecting you from the TV's radiation, considering the acceptability of water towards bioenergy. In Europe, there are many different devices concerned with this matter, but are pretty much out of reach. An American company started the production of Tachyonized merchandise which is quite promising in negative energy protection. Tachyon energy is same as Chi, Prana or bioenergy and was defined by Gerald Feinberg in 1966 as faster-than-light, subatomic particles. The name has been in use since the late 1800's and was highly popularized by one of the greatest scientists of our century: Nikola Tesla. The inventor of the alternating current generator, the fluorescent light, the wireless remote, and the brain behind the first hydro-electric plant went so far that he created a device which was able to convert Tachyon energy into electricity! In the second half of the 1930's he ran a self-made electro-mobile fueled by nothing but Tachyon! (Some authors claim that it was indeed a successful device, but was shut down at the very beginning because, even then, it would have destroyed the whole world economy!)

The so-called "Tachyonized" cells, creams, silica discs, gels, headbands, etc., are claimed to attract the free Tachyon energy, thus keeping its user energized all the time. I'm not very familiar with any serious experiments regarding these products, but I have tried them myself and could feel the energy around them.

Another product that I have tried was invented in Yugoslavia by an acquaintance of mine, Branislav Stojanovic, one of the first known biotherapists in the country. It is called Cosmogenerator.

The Cosmogenerator is a device for accumulation, amplification and direction of positive cosmic rays. It is made out of plastic and doesn't require any energy sources for activation. Its shape itself does the work! Mr. Stojanovic based

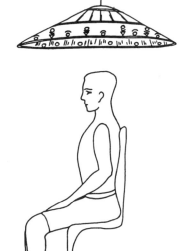

his contraption for personal use on the pyramid effect. If placed 10-30 centimeters (4"-12") over the body, it will focus the positive cosmic rays onto its user, thus filling up and eventually balancing the energy field. It really works! My family has been using it for over seven years, feeling its benefits. All it needs is some dusting from time to time. Many experiments have been conducted to prove the efficiency of the Cosmogenerator, among them installing them in a classroom over every student. Needless to say, the students' attention improved dramatically. Another tryout happened at a chicken farm, where after installation of the device, the growth of the chickens skyrocketed.

The size of the Cosmogenerator is 80 centimeters (32") in diameter, however, it has a smaller "brother" too, called "Cosmolok", which can fit in the palm of the hand. It is triangular in shape and is used 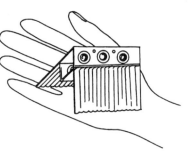 for unlocking local energy disturbances, for instance, arthritic pain of the wrist.

Even though it has received many international awards, as far as I'm informed Cosmogenerator is not sold in the USA. However, I'll be glad to give directions for its purchase to all the interested readers.

While we are talking about protection from negative energy, we have to mention the Faraday-cage. It is a metal construction which doesn't allow the transit of any electromagnetic fields in or out of it. However, experiments with telepathy show that a Faraday-cage is not an obstacle for accomplished telepathists, so we can't rely on this method for negative energy protection. Who would live in a cage anyway?

So far, the best protection known is recognizing the negative areas and avoiding them. As most of us are not able to purchase any "tracking devices", we have only one solution: Find help in the old skill of dowsing.

DOWSING TOOLS

Throughout the centuries, dowsing tools have been perfected and new ones invented by many to suit different needs in this field. The one that is probably best known to the general public is the "Y-rod". The name comes from the shape of the rod, usually an elastic branch of a tree. It has been used not only to find water, but for other purposes, too.

The following picture shows some of the most popular dowsing tools:

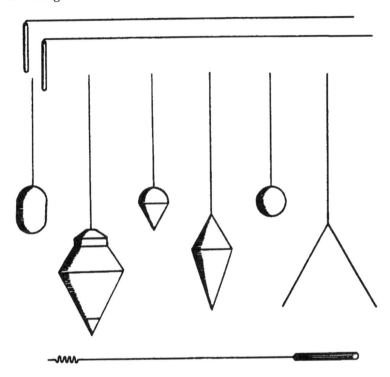

Before we go through the methods of using each dowsing tool, we must learn the basic principle of dowsing. How can a piece of wire or a hanging doohickey show us anything?

To answer this question, we have to go back deep to our subconscious mind.

Since we were babies, different reactions have been developed in our bodies for various inputs from the surroundings. The senses of the body pick up the data and send impulses to the brain for processing. The brain then registers everything and sends back signals to various parts of the body as a reaction. Throughout this process our mind makes a selection and divides all the available data into two opposites which then go to the endless storage space of our subconscious. The two opposites are chosen by our reaction to the input. They are either pleasant or unpleasant. The entire process may be connected to the theory of Yin and Yang of the Eastern philosophy: We react differently to warm and cold, dark and light, male and female, positive and negative, good and bad, etc. Some inputs cause rapid reactions in the body, for instance the "fight-or-flight" syndrome[2], while others we don't even register.

All these signals are so strong by the time we are mature, that our bodies turn into reliable sensors. Remember, our bodies are able to feel the energy of the surroundings, even though we don't pay attention. So, what do we need to utilize these powerful sensors? Instruments, scales, or indicators, or simply: dowsing tools. The light, delicate extensions of our arms are able to show the slightest moves of the "sensor", which enables us to tap into our subconscious minds with minimal effort.

The best tool to start with is the pendulum. There is a great variety of pendulums. They may be sharp, spherical, long, or short, and made out of virtually anything. The usual material is copper, silver, or gold (good conductors), but you can find crystal, ceramic, or stone-made pendulums, too. Experienced dowsers use different pendulums (or dowsing tools) for different tasks. For the beginning, however, a ring or a [screw] nut will do it as well.

------

[2]The fight or flight syndrome is caused by the Sympathetic Nervous System as a reaction to a sudden stress situation. As a result the heart beats faster, most blood vessels constrict, blood pressure increases, blood vessels in skeletal muscles dilate, sweat glands and adrenal glands secrete more abundantly, etc. Together, these responses make us ready for strenuous muscular work as they prepare us for fight or flight.

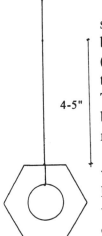

4-5"

Take a medium sized nut and tie it to a thin string or thread. The length of the line should be slightly longer than the width of your hand (five fingers). Tie a knot on the line to mark the length exactly five fingers from the nut. This is the spot you are supposed to hold between the forefinger and the thumb of your right hand (if you are right handed).

Holding the string in the above described way, relax your wrist and elbow and let the nut hang without shaking. Now, you have to learn which signals your body is giving. Think hard of the answer "yes". Repeat it in your mind, or say it aloud if you wish. Soon, the pendulum will start circling in one direction: clockwise or counter-clockwise. Remember it well, because this is the direction it will always follow for the answer "yes".

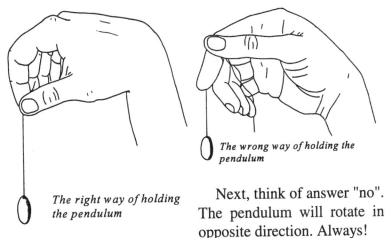

The wrong way of holding the pendulum

The right way of holding the pendulum

Next, think of answer "no". The pendulum will rotate in opposite direction. Always!

Most people will have no problem with these exercises. However, if the pendulum doesn't move right away, don't give up. Sooner or later 90% of you will get it!

Now, that you have established your answers, the door is wide open for further advancement in the art of dowsing. All you have to do is to ask [reasonable] questions, and you'll get the answer from your pendulum. The questions should always be formulated to get an answer of "yes" or "no". If for some reason it is impossible to get a straight answer, the pendulum will swing back and forth.

The opportunities are endless. You may try to surf in your subconscious, getting a date or some data you have forgotten. You may enquire about a health situation of yourself or another, do a calorie-count of your meal, and find the negative areas in your surroundings. Of course, it will take a lot of practice to be accurate, but if you are able to concentrate and clear your mind of all the outside distractions, you may become an excellent dowser.

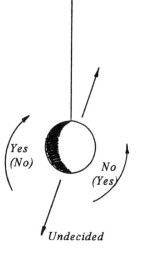

Yes (No)   *No (Yes)*

Undecided

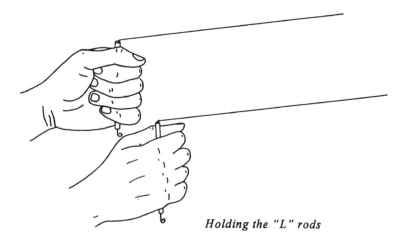

Holding the "L" rods

USING YOUR NEW SKILLS

Besides the pendulum, a helpful aid for getting accurate results is a "percentage diagram". It is a simple drawing on a piece of paper or cardboard, of a semicircle divided into ten equal segments by lines radiating out from the center. The diagram shows 100% of a measure with each section representing 10%.

To use a percentage diagram, you simply have to put the pendulum 1-2" above the center of the semicircle, and its oscillation will show the wanted amount.

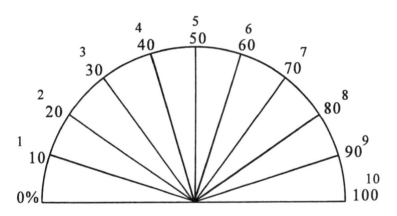

Example:
Holding the pendulum in the above described position, ask

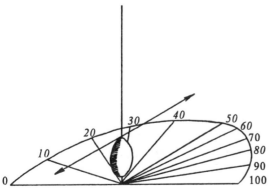

the question: If 100% of bioenergy in the body is the ultimate, what is the percentage of bioenergy in my body?

Answer (for instance): The pendulum oscillates towards the number 90, which means that the body has 90% of bioenergy.

Note: There are many ways to do an accurate diagnosis through dowsing, however, only a licensed professional is legally allowed to diagnose.

Once you have established the feel for your pendulum, you may widen the range of your questions by changing the "setting". Initiate new answers just by agreements made to yourself.

Here are some examples:

Agreement: The clockwise circling of the pendulum is the answer "yes", while counterclockwise is "no".

Question: Is the heart of the person NN healthy?

Answer: The pendulum circles clockwise, which means that the heart of NN is healthy.

Agreement: The clockwise revolution of the pendulum shows the ill areas, while for healthy areas the pendulum is motionless. The pendulum will react only to the areas touched by my left hand.

The task is to find the unhealthy areas of NN's body.

Result: The pendulum circles while my hand is over the kidneys, lower back and left knee, which means that those areas are not healthy.

Agreement: The pendulum will show the direction to the highest level of negative radiation in the room.

Result: The pendulum swings to a certain direction. In this case you have to repeat the procedure from another point in the room, so the crossing of the two directions will give you the exact spot you have searched for.

In all these cases you may find out the percentages, too. Put the pendulum over your diagram and simply ask: What is the percentage of bioenergy in the heart? What is the percentage of bioenergy in the knee? What is the percentage of negative energy under my bed?

FINDING THE NEGATIVE AREAS

As said before, there are negative areas all over the world. However, our concern is only the areas where we spend most of our time.

The first place you should check is the bedroom. Stand in one corner holding your pendulum and simply ask: are there any areas of negative radiation in this room?

If the answer is no, you have finished your work in that room. If it is yes, proceed to the next question. Holding your diagram ask: How many areas of negative radiation are in this room?

If there are many of them, ask: How many areas have negative radiation over 20% (which is considered harmful)?

If the answer is 3 (for instance), say: Show me the direction to the strongest area of negative radiation.

After getting the direction, move to a different spot in the room and repeat the command, so you can find the exact spot

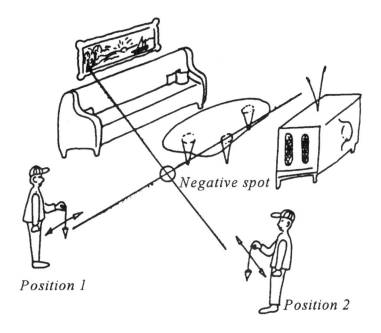

Negative spot

Position 1

Position 2

through the crossing of the two lines. Continue by asking (using the diagram): What is the percentage of the negative radiation in this spot?

If, for instance you get a readout of 40%, you may find out all about that radiation by asking how wide it is, where it comes from (underground water, TV, etc.), or if there is any way of protection against it. This way you will be sure if that area affects you at all.

In the same way you can find and check the other two spots, too. Again, make sure that your mind is completely relaxed and undistracted!

After finishing with the bedroom, you can check every room in the house, using the same method.

If you think it would take too long to measure the whole house, there is another, easier way to find all the negative areas. Take the ground-plan of your house, and by concentrating on it, ask the same questions: Are there any negative areas in my house? How many? Where? What is the intensity? You may even pinpoint the areas with a pen. The results will be as accurate as with the first routine.

Many people who have learned this method end up remodeling their houses and offices, which in most cases improves their health and overall mood. You will certainly find the benefits of this almost playful technique of the art of dowsing.

THE BIOENERGETIC CAPACITY

As we have found, everything in nature and the Universe constantly pulsates and radiates. From the tiniest atomic particle to the highest level of existence, there is a wide scale of various vibrations. These vibrations differ not only from one existence to another, but also from one individual to another. As there are no matching fingerprints, there are also no equal bioenergy fields.

As an experiment, you may find this out yourself through measuring other people's energy fields with the help of your pendulum.

The **Bioenergetic Capacity**, or the **Ability to Radiate** is a new term that we will use in order to determine how much bioenergy our body is able to transfer to other individuals.

Let's assume that 100% of bioenergy (what a healthy person possesses) is 1 unit of the same energy. That means that if you have 80% of bioenergy in your body it equals 0.8 units. This will be our measure for the bioenergetic capacity, or "BC".

Bioenergetic capacity does not equal the bioenergy in your body. It is purely your capability of emitting bioenergy. Although, everybody radiates a certain amount of energy, the beginning bioenergetic capacity is always below 1 unit. Some individuals, thanks mainly to their bodies' better conductivity, may develop that ability to a higher level under some circumstances even without knowing it. This may happen through patting or kissing a child who is hurt, or just by being very caring. They might perceive some tingling in their hands or sense heat while touching others. People close to them may feel the same. A very large percentage of these individuals - based on their experiences- will never proceed to become powerful healers, only because they can't explain the signals they are getting from their bodies.

Studies all over the world try to explain the phenomenon of radiating energy through examining famous healers. Some analysis shows better conductivity of the skin with these people, some claim the electric current in the body is the source of energy, while others swear to the power of the brain. As we'll learn later, telepathic and bioenergetic powers are not out of reach for any of us, moreover, we experience them every day.

The conclusion is that bioenergetic capacity may increase through a lifetime. The more energy we transfer, the higher the bioenergetic capacity becomes. So, how far can we go? Well, the sky is not the limit.

Each of us is born with a particular **Genetic Potential,** which determines the highest possible intensity of bioenergetic capacity we can attain. It is a gift. Some people are born to play piano, while others may practice a lifetime and never reach the same level. The most fortunate people are the ones who find their gifts and utilize them. Some of you might be gifted artists, and again, some of you may become famous teachers or... healers.

How do we get this genetic potential? By birth. However, measuring through dowsing shows that this gift may come only from one parent, contrary to other hereditary qualities that are usually a combination from both parents. That means we are getting it without any changes. There are no rules concerning which parent's genetic potential is inherited by which child. One child might get a strong genetic potential, while the other will get a weak one. It is possible that one will inherit its father's bioenergetic capacity, while the other will get its mother's, or they will both get it from only one of their parents.

The theory of genetic potential is very similar to the Chinese conception of the Chi. The basic Chi comes from the parents (Juan Chi-also called the "pre-birth" Chi). From food comes the grain Chi (Ku-Chi), and from air that enters our lungs comes the natural air Chi (Kung-Chi). The last one defines the Chi Kung (or Qi Gong) expression. Many healers and energy-balancing practitioners use this theory to enhance their energy, although it is a fact that the more you utilize your bioenergy the more you create.

So, what are our possibilities with this gift? How do we know how much potential we possess? The answer again is: Through dowsing.

Take your pendulum, hold it over the percentage diagram and just ask what is your genetic potential: "On the scale from 0-100, what is my genetic potential?" If it is undecided, try from 0-10. If the pendulum is still just circling around, try to get a lead by simply asking without the diagram: "Is my genetic potential between 0 and 200?" or so, until you get an approximate value and only then take the diagram to determine the exact number. It might be over 100, who knows?

Dowsing indicates that about 15% of people possess a minimal genetic potential of 5 units of bioenergetic capacity (BC). 30% of people have it between 5-10, while another 30% are in the range of 10-15. With the raising of the value of the genetic potential, this percentage rapidly drops, as you will see.

Genetic Potential of the Population

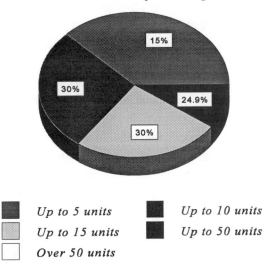

	Up to 5 units		Up to 10 units
	Up to 15 units		Up to 50 units
	Over 50 units		

There are three major groups of people characterized by the distinction of possibilities in using their genetic potential. In the first group are the individuals with genetic potential under 15 units. They make up about 75% of the population. The second group consists of individuals with a genetic potential between 15 and 50, which makes up about 25% of the population. The third group, with genetic potential over 50 units, makes less than 0.1% of people.

An old theory states that people in the first group may radiate only with their hands, while the second group is able to radiate with the "third eye", too. Only a small fraction of people-the third group- is able to radiate with the solar plexus and the brain. This belief, however, has never proved itself in practice. Many people using either Silva's Mind Control or other meditation techniques to perform long distance healing, do not have high genetic potential, but still get fantastic results. In those cases the energy doesn't come through the hands!

In practical use, if we take that laying on of hands is our basic measure for radiation (100%), then a hand held about 4" above the body is about 5% more effective. If the same hand circles on that distance, it will emit almost 90% more bioenergy than the unmoving hand. Radiation through the third eye will be three and a half times more effective than the basic value (350%). The same goes for radiating through the brain. Some claim that the solar plexus is the absolutely most effective way of radiating, with a value of over 900% higher than of the basic hands-on radiation.

The intensity of the sensation of the receiver, however doesn't reflect these measurements. While the strongest perception is triggered by the hand radiating through circling on a certain distance from the body, the recipient will hardly feel anything from a radiation coming from the brain or solar plexus. This fact actually makes any technique compatible, because, while the third eye radiation is more effective, the sensation of the recipient of the circling hand technique will balance out the difference through a positive mental attitude. This gives us a wide range of choices among methods to use.

The largest difference between the genetic potentials (or abilities to radiate) is in actual time spent on treatments. While someone, for instance, with a genetic potential of 5 units, needs ten to fifteen minutes to relieve a headache, the same task will take only a few minutes for somebody with a genetic potential of 50 units.

The following table compares the length of the necessary radiation with the ability to radiate, in order to alleviate a light ailment. The result in all cases is 100% of bioenergy, or perfect health.

Bioenergetic Capacity	Number of Treatments	Length of Each Treatment	Energy Level Before	Energy Level After
10	25	3 min.	80%	100%
50	10	90 sec.	80%	100%
90	5	20 sec.	80%	100%

As we see, all our imaginary therapists have done a good job, however, the person with the least ability to radiate had to spend much more time than his colleague with the highest bioenergetic capacity.

Unfortunately, this same pattern can not be applied to serious illness, which requires stronger bioenergetic capacity.

Our next example shows four biotherapists treating a serious illness that has only 30% of bioenergy:

Bioenergetic Capacity	Number of Treatments	Length of Each Treatment	Energy Level Before	Energy Level After
3	70	30 min.	30%	50%
10	30	20 min.	30%	75%
50	20	3 min.	30%	100%
90	10	1 min.	30%	100%

Note: The length of the treatments in both examples show the actual radiation time, not the whole procedure! [3]

Our sample clearly demonstrates the supremacy of the higher bioenergetic capacity. However, even the biotherapist with the least ability to radiate achieved a 20% rise in the bioenergetic level of the treated person, which might not be "total health" but certainly is a lot of help.

HOW TO INCREASE YOUR BIOENERGETIC CAPACITY

First, you have to determine your basic energy levels, both the quantity of bioenergy in your body and the bioenergetic capacity. Again, keep in mind that anyone is able to radiate, no matter what the numbers are. Very important to know is that in order to work on others, your own bioenergy level has to be 100%!

So, how do we enhance our bioenergetic capacity? Easy. By radiating! The more we radiate, the higher the ability to radiate. You may compare it to running: the more you run each day, the longer the distance you can run without getting tired. There is a difference, however. If you stop running for a while, your aerobic capabilities will gradually decrease. On the contrary, your bioenergetic capacity will always remain on the highest level you have achieved (although it will not increase without further work).

To follow your progress, you should again use your pendulum and percentage diagram. It is very helpful if you measure your energy levels every day and take notes.

---

[3]Both tables are taken from the book <u>Bioenergy - A World Without Illness</u> by Branislav & Ljubisa Stojanovic

For better understanding, let's take NN for example. The level of bioenergy in his body is 60% because of some local imbalances. His fundamental (basic) bioenergetic capacity is 0.45 units. If he would radiate himself every day for: a) 1 hour, b) 30 minutes, c) 15 minutes, then his bioenergy level would reach 100% in: a) 10 days, b) 20 days, c) 30 days. During that period his bioenergetic capacity would grow to: a) 0.8, b) 0.85, c) 0.9 units.[4]

NN should continue this practice until he reaches at least 1.5 units of bioenergetic capacity if he wishes to treat others, too, for that is the minimal value to keep your own bioenergy level around 100%.

Most people have an initial amount of bioenergetic capacity between 0.05 and 1 unit, while it is a rare exception to have it over 1 unit. So, for the general population here is the guideline, again:

Bioenergetic capacity increases proportionately with the applied radiation, up to the genetic potential of each individual.

This means that no matter how low your initial abilities are, with hard work and lot of practice you will be competent to heal the sick and preserve your health.

ENABLING TO HEAL OTHERS

After you have attained a minimal bioenergetic capacity of 1.5 units, you may start working on others, too. Your progress will be easy to follow through dowsing, but simple math may also help you to predict the outcome.

The two factors determining the speed of your advancement are indeed the initial bioenergetic capacity and the daily time spent on radiation. Your bioenergetic capacity will

---

[4]From <u>Bioenergy - A World Without Illness.</u>

proportionately grow until you are up to 15 minutes of radiation a day, while after that time the development will gradually slow down and reach its end after an hour of radiation.

For a bioenergetic capacity of 1.5-5 units, fifteen minutes of radiation will increase that capacity by 0.1 unit. Over 5 units of bioenergetic capacity may grow by 0.2 or even 0.3 units over the same or longer period of time (usually 0.3 for 30 minutes of radiation). Keeping this in mind will help you count ahead to see how many days and how much daily radiation you'll need to obtain a certain level.

Example:

The beginning bioenergetic capacity is 1.8 units. Radiation goes on for seven days, fifteen minutes a day.

$1.8+7x0.1=2.5$

Consequently, the new bioenergetic capacity is 2.5 units.

Question: If the initial bioenergetic capacity is 1.4 units, how many days is it necessary to radiate 30 minutes a day to reach 5 units?

Answer:

$5-1.4=3.6$

$3.6/0.2=18$ days

Question: How many days is it necessary to radiate 30 minutes a day to reach a genetic potential of 35 units, if the current bioenergetic capacity is 5 units?

Answer:

$35-5=30$

$30/0.3=100$ days

Naturally, all these calculations give only rough results, but good enough to follow your development.

When the final genetic potential is reached, there is no further advancement. However, choosing the right method of radiation may multiply your abilities. As said before, some methods are more effective than others, although to be able to use them   -according to some authors- it is essential to have a certain level of bioenergetic capacity.

If, for instance, your genetic potential is 35 units (and let's assume that you have reached it), then your maximum radiating power through hands-on radiation is naturally 35 units. However, if you hold your hand about 4" above the body, the capacity will be 5% larger, which means that you'll radiate 35x1.05=36.75 units. If you circle your hands on the same distance, the capacity will be 90% more effective, raising your radiation ability to 35x1.9=66.5 units! The same way your radiation ability will grow to 35x3.5=122.5 units if you radiate with your third eye! Again, your capabilities are limited by your genetic potential, which has to be at least 15 units in order to radiate with your third eye, and at least 50 units to radiate with the brain and the solar plexus.[5]

The third eye is located in your forehead, between your eyebrows, while the solar plexus is between the sternum and the navel.

Contrary to radiation through the hands, which has several different techniques and movements, when using the third eye, the brain, or the solar plexus, it is not necessary to be near the patient, nor turned towards the same. In addition, radiation through the hands will- besides the target organ- also radiate the surrounding organs, while through the other techniques it is possible to radiate a specific organ, or even a small segment of it.

Also important to know is that after a lot of practice and work with your hands, the radiating process will go virtually automatically, while to use the other methods you have to concentrate all the time.

---

[5] As said before, you may overcome this limitation through certain meditation methods.

THE QUALITIES OF A GOOD HEALER

Medius curat natura sanat.
Doctor treats, nature heals.

I have to emphasize it again: The only way to heal others is with love. You have to love what you do, and you have to love each person you treat. You can't heal someone only with your body, you must include your mind and your soul as well.

Being a good healer doesn't mean that you have to be a professional. You might want to do it as a "hobby", helping your friends and family. Regardless, there are some requirements and precautions you have to keep in mind.

To heal others, you have to be in perfect health yourself! This has been said before, but it doesn't hurt to repeat. If you don't stick to this rule, you may cause more harm than good. A good healer constantly seeks the perfect mental and physical balance.

Never underestimate the problem, be objective. Always be positive, but try not to give false hope. Each person is so different that it is almost impossible to predict the outcome. A measure of accuracy comes only with experience. So, let time show you what to expect.

Learn about the person you are getting ready to work on. See if he/she needs encouragement. Some people are negative by nature, or might have lost hope for improvement. They need to get all the positive attitude you can give. A very helpful way to improve these "negative vibes" is through group therapies.

GROUP THERAPY

A group therapy is done practically in an entertaining manner. Everybody in the group is allowed to talk and ask questions while the therapist works on each individual - one at a time. The best setup is if you have no more than 10-15 people sitting in a circle around you. While you work on one person, ask the others to sit with their feet and hands separated, possibly palms turned up. Some of them will feel a slight tingling or heat in the palms of their hands or even in other parts of their body. That itself is a good sign, very encouraging to the nonbelievers. As the treatments go on many people will tell the others what they sense and how their bodies are reacting. What is even better, the next time the group meets, ask everyone to tell about the changes since the last treatment. There are always individuals who have improved significantly, a notion which changes the group thinking towards the positive. "If he helped that person so much, I can also expect a lot of improvement."

Don't get me wrong, biotherapy works even without the person believing in it (just think about healing babies, animals, or plants), but if they do believe and trust, half of your work is already done. The greatest healer is indeed inside people's heads, the only problem is reaching it!

After the initial groups, as the word spreads, your job gets easier, too. After everybody learns that this is not some hocus-pocus, the general viewpoint will lean towards the positive.

Through my own experience I have learned that group treatments speed up the time of healing by up to 50%, thanks to more trust and belief from the patients, which in the long term cuts the energy and time requirements. My favorite method of quickly changing people's attitudes is to shock them: At our first session, while I explain what biotherapy is, and what I'm going to do, I choose a person that I'm absolutely sure is very susceptible to bioenergy. I ask that person to be the first to be worked on, and just startle everyone by pushing or pulling him/her without any touch. Then I demonstrate the same from the other side of the room, further from my subject. Sometimes lifting an arm without touch is enough. To make sure of the effect, I'll do that with somebody else, too, although many times I have done it to the whole group! You may guess what is going on in their minds: "If he can do that, he can definitely help me!"

Don't be discouraged if you can't give such a performance. It is enough if you just take a person's headache away in front of everybody!

From the very beginning write a case history about every person you treat. It also helps if you treat only certain problems at a time. For example, if you treat only headaches for a while, you will establish a nice pattern to follow in the future for better results. Experience is hard to get, but once you have it, you'll never lose it. Be patient!

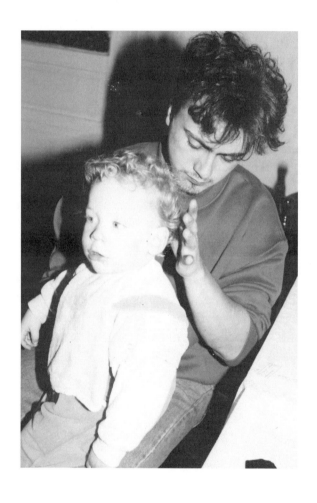

ENERGY ENHANCING EXERCISES

One rule remains: The more you radiate, the more energy your body generates. Consequently, to enhance your energy level, all you need is to practice your skills. Of course, as you already know, more energy requires less time radiating and faster recovery. So, the higher the bioenergetic capacity you reach, the more proficient you become - all the way to your genetic potential. The question you may ask yourself is: Is there a way to speed up the progress? Or: How do I maintain my energy level after reaching the "top"- the genetic potential?

The answer to both questions is the same: through exercises. "Classical" exercises consist of movements, involving some or all of the body parts. Whether they are aerobic exercises (running, biking, swimming), or weight-lifting, or any other kind of workout, they all affect the muscular and cardio-vascular systems of the body. Practicing on regular basis will strengthen these systems to a certain level, which depends on many factors.

There is a huge variety of sport enthusiasts, ranging from those who consider a 30 minute walk a good workout, to the professional athletes who perform strenuous exercises for over six hours a day. The difference between these extreme groups is that the first group fulfills only a minimum daily workout, required by the average physique. The second group, however, constantly enhances the body's strength and endurance, letting it evolve to a higher level. Very often, reaching the limit, or even surpassing the threshold of pain, will lead to a feeling of well-being, or euphoria, thanks to the body's natural pain killers, the endorphins.

The bioenergetic capacity of the body also follows similar guidelines. Although the ability to radiate- once the genetic potential has been reached- remains more or less the same, your own health and the effectiveness in healing others greatly depends on how good a shape your energy field is in.

Although it is important to have a healthy body in all aspects, that is not enough to improve the energy levels. You must include your mind in the process. That's right, the mind is the main coordinator of the energy. In a previous chapter you learned that the mind is the most powerful way to radiate, but you are still not sure how it works. In this chapter we'll discuss some energy enhancing exercises that use the power of the mind, and some that combine the mind power with certain body movements and positions. If you can master these techniques you have a good chance to learn long-distance healing!

Before we start, please set aside at least half an hour a day for practice. All these exercises require some commitment, and even after mastering them it is necessary to continue doing them on regular basis just to maintain the knowledge, and the level of energy.

The ancient Chinese ideology claims that there are three different types of Chi. The first one we acquire at birth, the second one comes through the food we eat, and the third one enters our systems through the air we breathe. While we can not influence the first one, the other two are indeed under our control.

As far as food is concerned, I wouldn't like to gabble about it too much, considering there are plenty of books available on healthy diet. Breathing however, is such a substantial part of our lives that most of people don't pay any attention to it. We know that we breathe more heavily when we exercise, or when we get excited, and we also know that we cannot hold our breath for a long time. But, have you ever listened to your body after a good aerobic exercise? Even though you get tired, it feels good, right? Besides all the chemical processes that take place in your system (like the release of endorphins), there is a great deal of bioenergy that you capture through elevated breathing. It is pretty chaotic, but it is there. There are many ways to turn that chaos into a fruitful source of energy, primarily by focusing on the breathing either through concentration or meditation, or through special exercises.

The most complete energy enhancing exercises that are the closest to the "conventional" exercises come from the Orient, where the concept of energy has been accepted for thousands of years. Some of these exercises, like Yoga, T'ai Chi and Qi Gong, have spread all over the world in the past few decades, enjoying a well-deserved popularity.

YOGA

The oldest system of mind, body, and spiritual exercises in the world is believed to be founded by the god Siva in ancient India. Archeological evidence puts the origins of yoga at approximately 3000 BC. Literally meaning "joining", yoga is originally practiced to unite the individual "self" with the "pure consciousness".

The importance of yoga as an energy-enhancing exercise is seen through the five major principles of this art. They are:

-**Correct Exercise** through yoga postures. Systematically working on all parts of the body, they stretch the muscles and ligaments, and maintain the flexibility of joints, while cultivating the circulation of blood, lymph and the energy (Prana).

-**Correct Breathing.** Yoga teaches one to use the full capacity of the lungs, this way controlling the flow of prana, which recharges the mind and the body.

-**Correct Diet**. Well balanced and nourishing, this keeps the body flexible, resistant to disease, and calm in the mind.

-**Correct Relaxation** releases tension in both body and mind, teaching you calmness and energy preservation.

-**Meditation**. Being the foundation of all the positive thinking, this calms the mind and organizes the thoughts.

Yoga can be extremely helpful in restoring your body's energy, however it needs a lot of devotion from a beginner. Seeing the masters of this art in their routine can scare off many people by causing them to doubt their own abilities. As many other exercises, yoga also requires a lot of practice, so if you choose to do it, find yourself a good teacher to show you the path.

It is impossible to explain yoga without writing a whole book. Yet, I have to mention at least one exercise. As simple as it looks, it is an exceptionally relaxing position, which I'm sure you have experienced before.

The Corpse Pose

Traditionally practiced before, between and after each session, this position yields your whole body to gravity.

Lie down on your back with feet separated and slightly turned out, and arms a few inches away from the body, with palms turned upwards. Close your eyes and relax. Perceive the force dissolving your whole body into the ground. Breathe deeply, but naturally with your abdomen. Relax...

As a preparation, you may want to stretch out your arms, legs, neck and low back by rotating and forcing them away from the trunk, then letting them fall to a loose position.

A wonderful way to relax and fight stress, this position is also a good preparation for meditation sessions.

T'AI CHI

T'ai Chi, the centuries old Chinese martial art and energy enhancing workout, has been re-discovered in the United States as one of the most efficient forms of exercise ever developed. It not only conditions the body, but also increases one's mental energy and reduces stress.

Originating in the last years of the Ming Dynasty (1368-1644), T'ai Chi has undergone 19 generations of development and perfection. For a long time, T'ai Chi was kept a secret within a few families, taught only to blood relatives, until the mid-nineteenth century when the Yang family, headed by the famous Wu Shu master, Yang Luchan, started teaching the general public, too. Since then, T'ai Chi has grown in popularity so much that it is now known to most of the world. For many years, visitors to China were astonished by the gracious, slow movements of T'ai Chi, done by virtually everyone in the early morning hours. Now it is available to all of us.

It is said that everyday practice of this art will give you the strength of a young man and the wisdom of the elderly.

The full name, T'ai Chi Ch'uan (or Taijiquan) means: the "supreme limit" or "Grand Terminus Boxing". Generally, it is no longer taught as a martial art in the western world. Although, through years of practice, one can achieve a great self-defense technique, T'ai Chi is known mainly for its health benefits and is recognized worldwide by medical experts as an effective way to control arthritic pain, promote cardiovascular fitness, and fight stress.

T'ai Chi is not just an ordinary exercise. As a part of the rich cultural heritage of China, it is an art in whose slow and gentle movements are embodied vigor and force. "Inside the cotton is hidden a needle," the Chinese saying claims.

Based on the laws of nature, using elementary biomechanics, T'ai Chi emphasizes breathing, balance, proper posture, and concentration, which eventually leads to an ultimate relaxation. The graceful, slow, fluid movements, combined with correct mental attention provide the practitioner with a complete mind and body exercise. Hence, many call it the Moving Meditation.

"Yielding overcomes the rigid." This Chinese saying refers to the power of the water, which is soft and harmless, but if constantly dripping, will make a hole in a rock. T'ai Chi follows these natural rules, and while other martial arts express more muscular strength and speed on the "outside", its power is on the "inside". Instead of using force, T'ai Chi accentuates using the mind. The internal strength gained this way is indeed the Chi!

We know that if the Chi meets an obstacle while "flowing" through the body, or through the meridians, it will eventually lead to sickness. While biotherapy or acupuncture help the body heal by "opening" the blocks, T'ai Chi helps prevent the forming of these barriers. Everyday practice moves the Chi throughout the whole body, thus keeping the passages/or meridians unobstructed.

To practice T'ai Chi, you don't need a special uniform or equipment, and you can do it anywhere and anytime. Daily practice takes as little as 15-30 minutes. It won't give the heart or cardiovascular system much of a workout, but it conditions and tones muscles, improves flexibility and balance, reduces stress, amplifies the lung capacity, and most of all increases your bioenergy levels. The best place for practice is outside in clean air, far from noise and pollution, wearing comfortable shoes and clothing.

There are many different types and schools of T'ai Chi. If you are seriously interested in studying this wonderful lifestyle, you should look for a good instructor in your area. Although there are several books and video tapes available on the subject, the most you can learn through them are the movements. To understand and experience the energy beyond those movements, it is necessary to learn from an accomplished teacher.

I have been teaching T'ai Chi since 1993, thanks to Mrs. Kim Hoover, who encouraged me to take over her classes after she moved out of this area. At times I have instructed over seventy students a week, most of whom were senior citizens. This fact made me adjust to easier exercises, teaching the Yang style only once a week, and dedicating the rest of the classes to more understandable and relaxed workouts. Mrs. Hoover taught me the Eighteen-Form T'ai Chi Qigong Exercise, which was the most suitable for the needs of my students. Through teaching it, I have made some changes in the form, incorporating some stretching techniques, Qi Gong warm-up's, and energy-awareness exercises, all to the benefit of my students and myself.

Note: I don't consider myself a T'ai Chi master, because I'm not. I hope I haven't offended any traditional T'ai Chi expert by making these changes.

In the following, I will try to explain the eighteen stationary exercises, hoping that you can also benefit from their graceful, energy-enhancing motions.

When starting your T'ai Chi workout please follow these rules:
- Your posture should always be relaxed, but straight.
- Keep your feet parallel, shoulder-width apart, with your pelvis slightly tilted forward (tucked under), and knees bent.
- Let your whole bodyweight sink into your feet, while imagining that a string is attached to the top of your head, holding you upright. Root yourself into the ground!

- Your breathing should be deep and relaxed.
- Always inhale through the nose and exhale through the mouth.
- Try to concentrate only on the exercise; clear your mind of everything else.
- You should repeat each exercise 8 times (or as many times as is comfortable).
- Always take your time. Remember, you are exercising for your own benefit!

The Eighteen Steps

1. Commencing Form and Regulating Breathing

Besides being the first form, every other form starts and finishes with this one. Stand in the basic, horse-riding stance: Feet are parallel, shoulder-width apart, knees slightly bent, pelvis tucked under, trunk upright, head straight, with relaxed chest, shoulders and arms.

Take a deep breath as you lift your hands- palms up- to nose level imagining that you pick up air (or energy). Keep your fingers, wrists and elbows relaxed all the time. As you reach the top, turn your palms down, and as you exhale, lower your hands to the starting position. Repeat eight times, without stopping, trying to connect the end of the previous movement to the start of the next. As you progress, you might be able to sense the energy moving up and down your front, as your hands move in the same path.

You may find this single exercise very helpful in calming you down in any stressful situation.

2. Expanding Your Chest

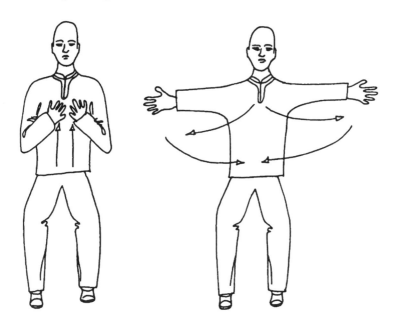

Start the same way as the first exercise, except, lift your arms only to mid-chest level. Then, turn your palms outward and extend the arms forward, away from the body. With a deep breath, stretch the arms horizontally to the sides as far as you can reach. Then, as you exhale, lower the arms to your sides, and finish by taking a deep breath as in the first exercise (commencing form). Also repeat eight times.

3. Dancing Like the Rainbow

Starting position: Still standing in horse-riding stance, lift your arms over your head, with palms turned in, as you were holding a beach-ball. Take a deep breath, and as you exhale, shift the bodyweight to the right leg and lower the "ball" to the left, as far as you can comfortably go. Keep your right arm over your head, not in front of it! Hold only for a split second, then go back to the starting position while inhaling. Repeat to the other side. Do the above movements eight times in each direction.

4. Circling Arms to Separate the Clouds

From the basic position, bend your knees and reach down, as you were scooping water, with hands crossed, keeping the left hand in the palm of the right. Now, stand up as you inhale, and reach up over your head as far as you can. Turn your palms outward, and as you exhale, with straight arms, slowly lower your hands to a natural position by your sides, while moving all your fingers- as you were sprinkling the water you just picked up. Finish by taking a deep breath as in exercise #1.

5. Swinging Arms at Stationary Position

Note: Some of the names do not reflect the actual exercises, partially because of the difficulty of translation and because of the changes made in them.

This is probably the most complicated one. Before you start, take some time to learn the Bow Stance:

The easiest way to memorize it is to start from the horse-riding stance. Shift the bodyweight to the left leg, pick up the toes of the right foot and turn them outward ninety degrees, while pivoting on the heel. Now, shift the weight to the right leg, pick up the heel of the left, and turn it back forty-five degrees, while pivoting on the toes. Make sure your feet are firmly on the ground, back upright, pelvis still slightly tilted forward. Seventy percent of the bodyweight is on the right leg,

thirty on the left, the right knee being more bent then the left. Make sure the knee doesn't go past the toes! You are now in a right, forward bow stance.

Shift your weight back and forth a few times, just to get familiar with the posture and to find your balance. This is a typical martial art stance. It provides good balance and opportunity for quick retreat as well as for a powerful blow.

To turn around into a left bow stance, all you need is to shift your weight to your left leg, pick up the toes of the right, and while pivoting on the heel, turn the right toes towards the left toes, like pigeon-feet. Put your toes down and shift the weight over to the right leg. Now, pick up the toes of the left and while pivoting on the heel, turn the foot out into a left bow stance. Finish by shifting seventy percent of your weight to the left leg.

Now, that you know how to turn in bow stance, you may proceed with the exercise: From the basic stance get into a right bow stance, keeping your weight on the left leg. Align your trunk with the left foot (forty-five degrees) and raise your arms

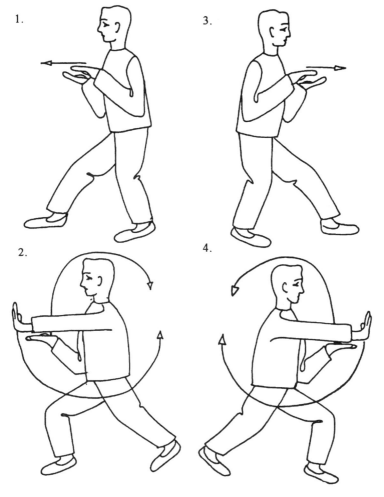

on the sides to shoulder level, palms facing up. Now, in a circle over the head, put the left palm over the right, and bend both elbows. Your fingertips are now aligned with the right foot. Slowly shift the weight to the right foot, and at the same time slide the left hand on the right until the left wrist reaches the fingertips of the right. As you finish this move, turn the left palm slightly up, into a pushing position. Now, drop both hands from the wrist and imagine picking up two strings. Bring them in towards the chest, turn the fingertips upwards, and with a deep breath expand the chest like in the second exercise. At the same time "sit back" by shifting the weight to the left, and turn the body to a left bow stance. Half-way through the turn, open the palms up, and you are in the starting position for the left part of the exercise. This time the right hand covers the left and does the push. Repeat eight times each side, and finish by taking a deep breath as in exercise #1, after getting back to the middle.

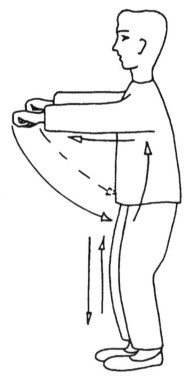

6. Rowing the Boat In the Middle of the Lake

Start in the basic stance, raising your arms straight in front of the chest. Make fists with your hands, as if you were holding oars. Now, lower your body by bending the knees, and let your arms swing by your sides, exhaling at the same time. After that, stand up and raise your fists close to the trunk up to shoulder level, bending your elbows, and inhaling at the same time. Now, push your hands to straight arms in front of the chest and start exhaling. Repeat the procedure in smooth motions, without stopping. Finish in the already established way, with exercise #1.

7. Carrying the Ball In Front of the Shoulders

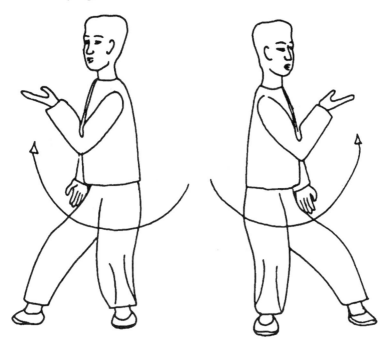

Imagine that you are holding a ball in your right hand. Take it to about a foot out in front of the left shoulder, holding it in your palm, while shifting the weight to the right leg. Now, drop the ball by turning the right palm down and slowly let your hand all the way down. Make a smooth turn to the right, at the same time shifting the weight to the left, and lifting the ball up with your left hand to the right shoulder. Note: the body turns slightly forty-five degrees towards the side on which you have the ball. Also, keep your arms moving at the same time (as one goes down, the other one goes up), and make sure your fingers, wrists and elbows are relaxed. Inhale as the ball goes up, exhale as it goes down. Repeat eight times on each side.

8. Turning to Look At the Moon

In horse-riding stance, with relaxed arms, hold the "ball" between your hands in front of you. Without moving your

feet,turn to the left, at the same time lifting the ball back and up
behind you, as if looking at the moon. Go as far as you can,
always staring through the ball. Let it down in the same route,
and without stopping, continue to the other side. Inhale as you
raise your arms, exhale as you lower them. Try to go further
with every turn.

9.Twisting Waist and Pushing Palms

From the horse-riding stance, get into a right bow stance in
the already established way. Put both hands, palms up, on the

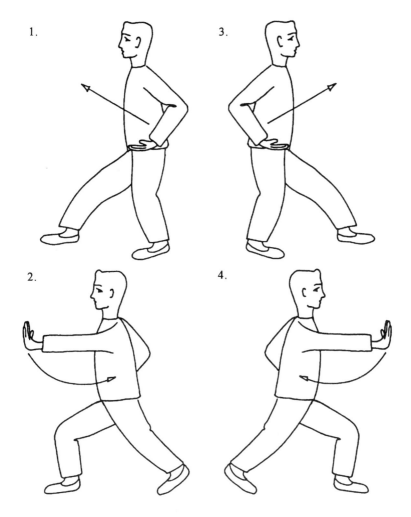

hips, while keeping the body-weight on the left leg. Now, slowly slide the weight to the right leg, at the same time pushing forward with the left hand, and exhaling. Try not to lock the elbow. Then, as if you were pulling back a rope, return your hand to the hip, while shifting the weight back to the left leg. Turn, and repeat on the other side. Again, make sure that your trunk is straight all the time. Try to push with the body weight that shifts on the legs, instead of the arms.

10. Riding a Horse and Swaying Arms

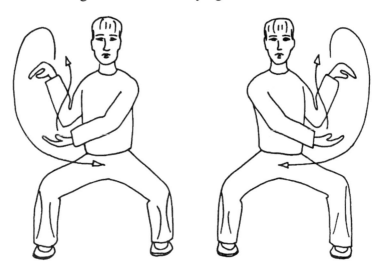

Widen the horse-riding stance, and lift your right hand to eye level, with palm turned slightly inward. Left hand should be relaxed, below navel. Turn to the right as far as possible, at the same time making a large circle with the right arm behind you. Coordinating with the right arm movement, lift the left hand to eye level, reaching it as the right hand gets to the position where the left hand was moments ago. Turn to the left, and repeat the above coordinated moves on that side, this time with the left hand making the wide circle. Always inhale as you make the circle and exhale as you do the turn. The above exercise can be executed in a more elegant and dancing-like fashion if you "wave" the lower arm while turning to the other side. Repeat eight times in each direction.

11. Scooping From the Sea and Looking At the Sky

From the horse-riding stance step out with the left foot forty-five degrees to the left to form a bow stance. Slowly make a motion as scooping water from in front of the left leg, just like in the exercise #4. Lift up the crossed hands as you bend backwards (sit back) and spread arms with palms facing

eachother when they extend overhead, while throwing your head back to look up at the sky. Inhale as you go back, exhale as you bend forward. Repeat four times in left bow stance, then step back and step out with right foot into right bow stance, and do another four repetitions.

12. Pushing the Waves to Help Bring In the Tide

Step out into a left bow stance, keeping the hands and wrists relaxed and palms turned downwards at approximately stomach level. As you shift your weight to the left leg, push out with your palms straight ahead to shoulder level, without stretching the elbow too far. Now, sit back, bringing the hands back to the trunk in a circle as if you were patting a large barrel on its top. Repeat the above push, this time extending the elbows a little bit farther.

Now, "bring the tide back" by letting your hands all the way down, with palms turned back. Sit back at the same time and bring the foot back to the middle. As you lift your hands to the beginning position, step out with the right foot, and repeat the above exercise. Inhale as you bring the hands to the trunk, and exhale as you push. Repeat eight times, changing the feet after "bringing the tide back".

13. The Flying Pigeon Spreads Its Wings

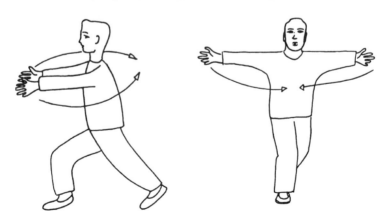

Step out into a left bow stance and extend your arms out from your sides at shoulder level, with palms facing forward. Take a deep breath. As you shift the weight forward, exhale and push palms horizontally towards each other, all the way until they almost touch. Sit back, at the same time bringing the hands back to the starting position and inhaling. Try to relax the hands, so that on the way back the fingertips follow the wrist. Repeat four times, then sit back, step out to a right bow stance, and do another four repetitions.

14. Punching With Outstretched Arms

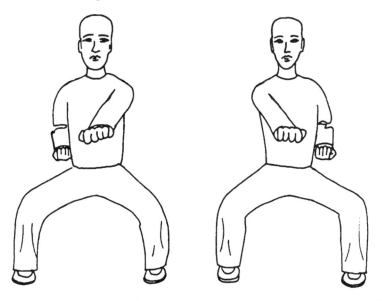

Stand in a slightly wider and lower horse-riding stance and place fists on hips with palm side up. Punch out straight in front of you to a mid-chest level, turning the fist palm down and exhaling in the process. Inhale as you pull the fist back to the starting position. Repeat with the other hand. Do the above movements eight times with each arm.

15. The Wild Goose Flying

Cross hands in front of the chest while standing in the horse-

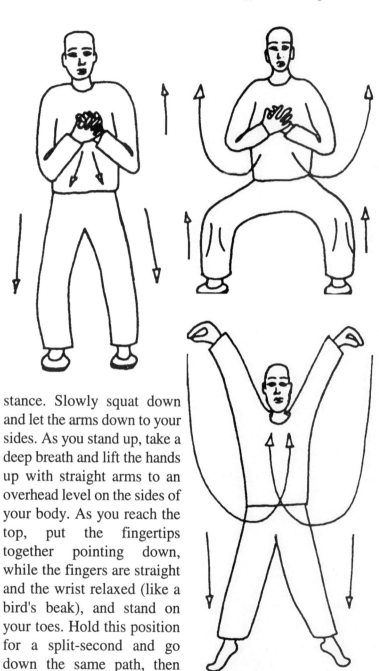

stance. Slowly squat down and let the arms down to your sides. As you stand up, take a deep breath and lift the hands up with straight arms to an overhead level on the sides of your body. As you reach the top, put the fingertips together pointing down, while the fingers are straight and the wrist relaxed (like a bird's beak), and stand on your toes. Hold this position for a split-second and go down the same path, then finish by standing up and crossing the hands in front of the chest. Repeat eight times, inhaling while standing up, and exhaling while going down.

16. Hands Turning Around Like a Wheel

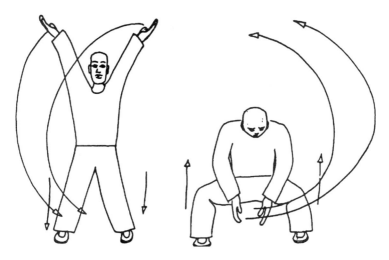

Keeping arms straight, with hands holding the imaginary ball, move them in four giant circles in front of you, first in one direction then in the other. Inhale when arms go up, exhale when they go down.

17. Bouncing a Ball With Leg Lifted

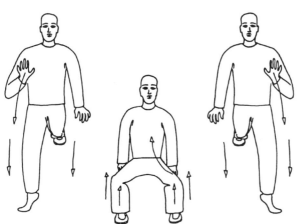

Lift the left knee and raise the right hand to s h o u l d e r level, then lower the right hand as if to bounce a ball while, setting the left foot on the ground and bending the knees. While standing up, do the same with the right knee and left hand, inhaling as the hand goes up, and exhaling as it goes down.

To make it more complicated- if you like challenges- stand up on the toes as you reach the uppermost position!

18. Pressing Your Palms In Calmness

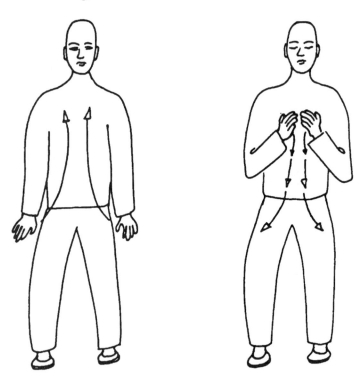

Take a deep breath as in exercise #1, but this time as you exhale, force the air out of your lungs, breaking down the exhalation into three bursts, with the first two being short and the last one letting out the rest of the air. Connect the hand movements (which follow the same path as in exercise #1) to the breathing! Repeat four times, or until calmed down.

I hope you have understood and enjoyed these exercises. Now, if everything went O.K., there should be a significant change in your energy field. Lift up your hands and hold the "ball". Can you feel the heat between your hands? Isn't it more intense?!

Qi Gong

As mentioned before, this ancient art can be traced back at least 2000 years (some claim even 3000 years!), long before Taoism or Buddhism spread to China. The early imitation of animal movements, like the dragon, birds, and others, has changed throughout history, resulting in thousand of styles and five major groups of Qi Gong exercises. It has also been gaining popularity throughout the world, just like T'ai Chi, thanks to its working wonders in preventing and curing disease, building up health, and tapping man's latent powers.

There are many books available on the subject, and most of the major cities have Qi Gong schools, so in the following I will try to present only a few interesting energy balancing exercises. You'll notice the similarities between these and the previous T'ai Chi movements.

Basic stance: It is exactly as described earlier in T'ai Chi. Feet are parallel, shoulder-width apart. Pelvis is tucked under, while the knees are slightly bent. Upper body and head are straight, as if a string were holding you as a puppet. Shoulders are relaxed, arms are hanging like ropes.

Try to hold this position for at least a few minutes, however, even an hour wouldn't hurt.

Basic Qi Gong

To balance the Chi in the whole body (in all the meridians), even one exercise is enough:

Stand relaxed with feet parallel in the above described way. Slowly lift up your forearms to make about a 90 degree angle with the relaxed upper arms. You may imagine that a string is attached to each wrist, holding the arms in position. At the same time bend your knees and turn the hands slightly towards each other. The wrists and fingers are also relaxed. Stay in this position for one or two minutes, then turn your palms down and hold for another minute.

After that, let your upper arms move backwards and out. In this position the forearms will gently dangle, while the palms are turned slightly backwards. Hold for about 30 seconds.

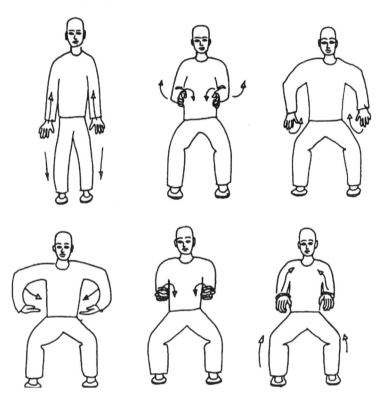

Now, turn the palms up in a gentle, circular way, with the fingertips facing the hips. After another minute, press the upper arms against the body, as the fingertips face forward with the palms still looking up. The angle between the upper and lower

arms is now less than 90 degrees, while the elbow is behind, not touching the body. Hold this position for a minute, then relax the squeeze and let the hands move forward, and again make the 90 degree angle between upper and lower arms. Try to relax in this position. You must hold it for 10-40 minutes (!), depending on the level of experience. Make sure the elbows don't touch the body, and the knees don't go past the toes. Breathing is natural, mind is relaxed. Some people even meditate in this position.

This stance supposedly speeds up the flow of the Chi in all the meridians. The purpose of the previous move, when pressing the upper arms to the body, is that for those few moments the blood concentrates at the shoulders, while after the release it will flow powerfully through the vessels, thus moving the possible obstacles away.

To finish this exercise, slowly bend your fingers, but not all the way into a fist. At the same time lift your hands up to shoulder level, stand up straight, and take a deep breath. As you exhale, gently let your hands down, with the palms facing down, and relax.

If you practice this exercise on regular basis, you may also experience the familiar heat in the palms of your hands every time you finish the set.

The Swings

The swings are very popular Qi Gong exercises. Besides energizing the internal organs as a basic function, they open up the joints of the hands, elbows, shoulders and hips. The loosening effects of the swings are simply remarkable.

1. The first swing is fairly easy: Stand in the basic horse-riding stance. Keeping your body upright all the time, start twisting your body from one side to the other. Turn your whole upper body and shoulders together. Your arms should be totally loose, like wet noodles! Relax them thoroughly from shoulders down, and let them swing. Once you accelerate and catch the momentum of the swings, your arms will carry your upper body with hardly any effort. As the speed increases, the arms will start slapping you, massaging the internal organs in the process. However, the loosening effect is more important than the hitting, so concentrate on letting your arms go until they totally "liquify".

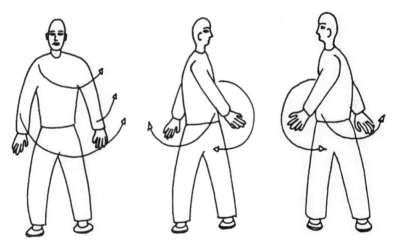

Do this exercise as long as you feel comfortable with it.

2. You may proceed with the second swing without stopping. Make a slightly wider stance, and as you swing, shift

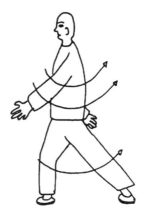

your body-weight from one leg to the other, always having it on the leg that you are facing at the end of the turn. Your trunk should remain u p r i g h t, however, and the knees must flex, having the larger bend on the leg that carries more weight. Everything else is the same as with the previous exercise.

3. The third swing may also be the continuation of the first two. This time as you twist to the left, shift the body-weight to the right leg and lift up the left leg just for a moment, then put the toes of the left foot on the ground at a 90 degree angle, that way preventing yourself from twisting all the way back. After you reach the end of the twist and

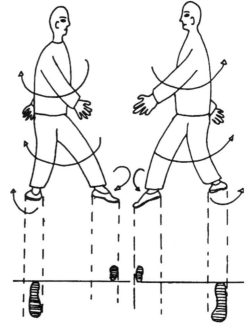

start turning to the right, place the left foot back to its original position. Before you reach the very end of the right twist, pick up the right foot, then place it on the toes at a 90 degree angle, while the body-weight is on the left leg. All the other parts of this swing are the same as with the preceding swings.

Meditation

Meditation is indeed the most powerful and hardest-to-learn energy enhancing exercise. Its intriguing goal- to tap into another dimension- has been motivating people for millennia to develop new ways to reach this extraordinary state of mind. Of course, by meditation I don't mean merely lying on the bed and looking at the ceiling.

The true essence of meditation is turning off all the senses and reaching a higher level of consciousness.

There have been many masters throughout history who were able to control their bodily functions on such a level that they could survive buried under ground for weeks without any consequences, while some people have been able to foresee the future, or perform other extraordinary tasks. They all agreed in one thing: their minds worked in a totally different dimension.

Today, a lot of people seek the help of meditation, mainly to fight stress. It is very relaxing to leave "this world", whether through hypnosis, self hypnosis, or any of the hundreds of varieties of meditation. However, many don't know that besides relaxation, meditation may be used for thousands of other purposes. If you apply it in the right way, it can help you solve everyday problems, such as which direction to take, where to go, when and how to apply for a job, organize your bills, etc. Besides these problems, you may also help your, and others' health, or simply program your internal clock to wake you up, or remind you of something. It is impossible to name all the advantages of meditation. The only way to find out is to do it.

Before you start any meditation, make sure you have all the conditions for a pleasant, relaxing atmosphere. There shouldn't be any noise, bright light, or other distractions.

Chose a cozy chair to sit in, unless you are comfortable in a cross-legged sitting position. Always keep your back and head straight. Later on, you may meditate in any position and anywhere you wish, but for now, try to follow these guidelines.

1. For your first exercise, sit down comfortably, and lock your sight on a spot straight ahead of you. As you relax, close your eyes and turn them slightly up, to about a thirty degree angle. This should help you open the "third eye", which is the energy center located on your forehead, just between the eyebrows. Your hands should rest on your legs, with the thumb, forefinger and middle finger touching at the fingertips on each hand. This position supposedly makes the ideal electromagnetic connection for meditation. For the same reason, it is also recommended to press the tip of your tongue up, against the palate. Breathe normally through your nose. Relax.

Try to keep the above procedure a standard for all the future meditations.

The following exercises are designed to lead your mind step by step to your final destination: the Alpha state of mind. It is not a new concept for your brain; you encounter it every day.

There are different types of brain waves, which are connected to three distinctive brain activities. When we are wide-awake our brain radiates Beta (β) waves, which are fast and small in intensity. During deep sleep our brain emits the ultra-slow Theta (θ) and even slower Delta (δ) waves. Alpha (α) waves, however, are very similar to the frequency that the Earth radiates, a fact which is used by some scientists to explain the phenomena it is responsible for. Our brain is in the Alpha state just before we fall asleep and right after we wake up. It is the time when we can still remember the dreams we had, but we are aware of our surroundings. This condition is called the Sophroliminal state. [1] In this state our brain has the unique ability to connect to the subconscious. The purpose of meditation is to teach the brain to tap into this state any time we desire. Although we are doing it every time we are daydreaming, it is much more challenging and rewarding to focus that power consciously. The better we are able to focus it, the stronger our energy becomes.

2. The emphasis is still on relaxation. Start in the way described under #1. Then concentrate on your body.

Relax your feet. Let them go until they seem to totally disappear. Now do the same with your legs, then your arms, your face, and finally the trunk. Just melt away, until you are aware of only your mind. It is much harder then it seems! You might need to talk to yourself during the process. For example: "My feet are getting mellow. There is a pleasant warmth in them. They are getting heavier and heavier until they are totally out of my control. I don't feel my legs at all..."

As a bonus exercise, you might want to concentrate on certain internal organs. After having everything under control, you may be able to regulate your breathing or even your heartbeat.

3. To get to a deeper relaxation try this method: After you have completed the above procedure, start counting from 100 to zero, while visualizing the numbers.

This exercise will force you to concentrate even harder. If you lose count, you have to start all over again! It will likely take you many tries before you succeed. Once you are

---

[1]Sophrology is a type of applied hypnosis, or self-hypnosis, with the emphasis on positive thinking, developed by Dr. Alfonso Caycedo in the 1960's.

comfortable with the count, you may begin by starting from a smaller number. It will take you less and less time to reach the Alpha state of mind. After a while you may establish your method of relaxation, or reaching the Alpha state by counting, for instance, from ten to zero. I usually count from three to one, repeating and visualizing each number three times, and connecting each number to one breath.

A subconscious command is also helpful: "I will count from ten to zero. When I reach zero, I will be totally relaxed and won't feel anything from my surroundings."

You may give another command after reaching zero: "Now, I'm totally relaxed, and I feel great. My mind works on a higher level of consciousness, and I will benefit from everything I do in this state."

Every time you wish to "come back" you may also use the numbers: "Now, I will count from one to three, and when I reach three I will be completely awake, feeling great and full of energy. 1...2...3." There is no limitation for these commands. You may also take care of some other problems, too. If for instance, you have a bad back, you may add: "... and my back will feel much better."

Avoid negative commands, as: "I will feel **no** pain", because they will be imbedded in your subconscious.

4. Visualization is one of the main elements of meditation, so let's do a few more exercises with it. Sit down in the position described in #1. You may also repeat the above exercises.
Now, close your eyes and imagine yourself sitting in the most comfortable chair. Try to feel the texture, see the color. Now, visualize yourself in a room, and decorate it as you wish. You may put a desk in front of the chair, with a clock and a calendar on it, pictures on the wall, chandelier on the ceiling, etc. Just use your imagination to make a cozy atmosphere. As a helpful device for future work in meditation, place a large white screen up in front of you.

During every meditation from now on, you may always return to "your room". It will make the concentration easier and will give you the sensation of peace.

5. This time we'll go further with the visualization. To enable your "inner vision" to accomplish more difficult tasks, I suggest the following exercise:

After repeating the previous routine, concentrate on the screen. Make sure you have no distractions, and see only the white color of the screen. Now, visualize your favorite fruit. If you don't have one, I suggest either an orange, lemon, or apple, because of the characteristic colors and aromas.

If you take an orange, for instance, put it on the screen and start seeing the contours. Then, focus on the color of orange. If you succeed, try to picture the little ridges on the fruit. Furthermore, try to touch it in your mind, or even smell it.

Your final assignment is to get into the orange! Yes, it is possible! Anything is possible on this level of consciousness. So, go into the orange, and see the inside. Examine the fine film that borders each slice, then get into an individual slice. Observe the delicate texture of a single sack holding the juice. Practice this exercise until you become completely flawless.

You may repeat this same meditation exercise with other subjects, too. Use your imagination!

As a final test, put yourself on the screen, and examine every aspect of your body, inside and out.

Once you reach perfection, you'll be ready for long distance healing.

Self-Hypnosis

If you have trouble concentrating, thus being unable to meditate, I suggest you try self-hypnosis. It is based on the same principles as meditation, however, in this case you may use a helpful tool: a tape recorder. After recording the whole process that leads you to the Alpha state, all you have to do is relax and listen to your own voice on the tape. Using self-hypnosis for a while will enable you to reach the meditative state easier and faster. Once you memorize the tape, you will be able to repeat the procedure on your own, with no help at all.

When recording the self-hypnosis tape, use a calm voice, speak slowly and clearly, and make sure there are no background noises. Remember that all the suggestions you make in the Alpha state of mind will stay imbedded in your subconscious.

Record the following text, or make up your own if you wish:

"I close my eyes and relax. My breathing is deep and even. With every breath I take, I sink deeper and deeper into a pleasant, soothing sensation... My eyes are shut completely, but loosely. My head is upright and relaxed. All I hear is my own voice. Now, I concentrate on my legs. They are getting heavier and heavier, with every breath I take. Slowly, I lose the feeling in my legs. They are there, but I don't feel them. I'm very relaxed... Now, I concentrate on my arms. They are also getting heavier and heavier. My shoulders, arms, fingers... they are all relaxed and heavy. Slowly, I lose all the feeling in them. They are so relaxed... My back is still straight, but very relaxed. All the muscles in my back are resting. They ease up so much that I slowly lose the feeling in them. My breathing is still deep and even. My heartbeat is relaxed. With every breath I take, I sink deeper and deeper in this pleasant feeling of warmth and darkness. Even though it is there, I don't feel my body at all. I'm very relaxed... All I can hear is my own pleasant voice. My breathing is slow and even, and I sink deeper and deeper...

In this pleasant state of mind, everything I say will stay deeply imbedded in my subconscious... Every time I listen to my voice, I will be relaxed and rested. All I can feel is a pleasant sensation of calmness... I can get out of it any time, but I don't want to. I feel good. I go deeper and deeper..."

After a few minutes: "Now I will count to three and open my eyes, and feel rested and very relaxed. With every count, I will feel my energy increasing and my body parts will wake up stronger than ever. One. I can feel the energy circulating through my arms, legs, and my trunk. Two. I feel I am waking, as if from a long, restful sleep. I feel energized throughout my whole body. Three. I take a deep breath, open my eyes and feel better than ever!"

When talking into the tape recorder, make sure to pause after every sentence. The slower it goes, the better.

Once you get used to your self-hypnosis tape, you may add some suggestions to the part before you "wake" yourself up. It may be forming the "screen" and imagining the fruit, or other suggestions. You may also be able to put yourself on the screen and examine your own body as in exercise #5.

I believe you will find the right energy enhancing exercise for your needs, and I hope I have made your choice easier.

LONG DISTANCE HEALING

As mentioned before, bioenergy is of electro-magnetic origin, but not quite as the electricity in classical terms. While the latter loses power proportionately to the distance it travels because of resistance, bioenergy may reach any part of the world with no loss at all. The vibration of this type of energy is such, that it permeates any known substance. Consequently, if we are able to influence someone's energy field without touch from a few inches away, we can do the same from much longer distances, too! This technique is indeed called Long-Distance Healing.

Mastering this skill will enable you to help not only someone who is not in your presence, but who is hundreds or even thousands of miles away!

As a pre-requisite for long-distance healing, you have to be proficient in meditation, especially the type taught in the previous chapter. Nevertheless, I will lead you on gradually, so you can get the hang of it.

For the beginning, chose someone you know to be your subject, preferably somebody you have worked on before. Of course, that person shouldn't be in your presence.

Make yourself comfortable, in the position you use for meditation. Go through the whole process of relaxation. Now, visualize the chosen person. See that person from every angle. It might take some time, but try to create a clear picture.

Now, be aware of your arms and hands. Get back all the feeling in them.

After that, start examining the energy field of your subject with your hands, just as if he/she were there. It might look awkward at the beginning, but once you realize how easy it is, it will turn into a lot of fun. Listen to your hands! They will pick up the same signals as when you worked on that person up close. The sensation of heat, cold, tingling, etc., will be almost exactly the same! Examine the whole body and memorize the areas of imbalance.

Now, put the energy field back to balance. Take off, or give energy through the same movements you have done before. Even though you are in meditative position, don't hesitate to move your hands in the already established manner. Also, don't forget to shake off the excess energy your hands have picked up. Finish the treatment in the same way as if that person were there.

As you see, everything is the same as before, except you have to concentrate and use visualization. You have to put the subject in front of you! The clearer the picture, the better results you can expect.

Naturally, to do a treatment this way, you don't have to stand up or walk around your subject. It is enough to "make" the person small and turn him/her around as desired.

This is also a good opportunity to try to visualize the energy field itself, not just the body.

To make it more interesting, here is what you can do: Tell your subject -wherever that person is- to sit or lie down comfortably with closed eyes, and relax, at the exact time when you work on him/her. After you have finished the treatment, call that person and ask for feedback. You'll be amazed. The outcome is sometimes so astounding that you won't believe it! The same sensations are experienced as in an up-close treatment.

You may of course, do a treatment anytime and anywhere, regardless of your subject's knowledge of it.

Keep on practicing, and when you feel you are ready, proceed to the next level.

This time the whole process will be done without the use of hands. For that reason, it is necessary to "open" the third eye, which will provide much better results.

Go through the whole process of relaxation and meditation again. When you get into your "room", form the familiar screen. Now, lift the screen a little bit higher, so your eyes will have to turn about 30-40 degrees up to look at it. That will ensure the exasperation needed to turn on the third eye. Not to worry, the unpleasant feeling will soon vanish. With enough practice, you will be able to use your third eye anywhere and anytime with no effort at all!

Now, put your person on the screen. Clear the picture and turn off all the distractions. Move your subject around. Take a good look from every side. Here comes the difficult part: Visualize your person's energy field. You might have to do it the classical way, moving the focus a little bit away from the body. See at least the first and the last layers. You don't have to see the colors, just see the energy. It might appear unclear and hazy, but the main goal is to see it.

Examine the aura by moving your sight from the top of the head to the bottom of the feet, first on the back, then on the front. See if you can spot any differences in the energy field. You may also go into the body to check out the internal organs.

After you have found the imbalances, you have to put the field back into balance, this time mentally, using your third eye. I have to emphasize again: Use your imagination! There are no limitations on how to employ your mind for the treatment. You may see yourself, or only your hands, doing the whole procedure. You may even imagine a vacuum cleaner sucking away the "dirty energy"!

There are unlimited variations in long-distance healing. The best way to do it is to program your mind from the very beginning. For example, you may command your subconscious to visualize all the imbalances in the energy field as gray, dirty areas, while the healthy parts could be pure white. That goes for both inside and outside the body. Once you get comfortable with it, you'll be able to spot the imbalances immediately, right after you make a picture of your subject.

You may also program your mind to see the chakras: White, precise cones if healthy, or gray and disfigured if out of balance.

Any which way you chose, try to develop a method that will fulfill your needs and stick with it. The more you practice the easier it gets!

After you have found the imbalances, first take the gray areas away through the method you have chosen. In other words, clean the aura. Then, generate a white layer of clean energy tightly around the body. You may take extra time to concentrate on the critical areas inside the body, and cover or fill those up with additional energy. The next step is to create new, healthy, white cones of energy to replace the old chakras. Finish by putting on the final, outer layer of the energy field.[1]

During long-distance healing, as in up-close energy treatment, additional mind-suggestions are also found to be helpful. Just "talk" to your subject in a positive manner, like: "You'll be fine", or "your pain will change into a pleasant feeling", or "your intellectual energy will increase", etc. These mental commands also carry the message of love, which inevitably multiplies the effect of your treatment.

Your final test in long-distance healing is to work on someone you have never met.

Recall the fact that we are all connected by the means of energy, so the distance and location are not of our concern. The key is to consciously unite your energy with your subject.

---

[1] In case of concentrating only on the first and last layer.

To probe your skills, you will need someone's help. Ask a friend to get you a picture of somebody he/she knows, but you are not familiar with. As an addition, ask for the name, age and approximate location of that person.

Study the picture and the data thoroughly, then go through the whole process of long-distance healing. Examine every aspect of your subject's body and energy field and memorize it. If it is not a distraction, ask your friend to write down the procedure as you describe it. Balance the energy field and finish the treatment.

Question your friend about your accuracy, or ask him/her to call your subject for more details.

If you feel you are ready, repeat the above test without the help of a picture. Put your accuracy on trial. Through the name, age and location of a new subject, make your own picture of that person. Dictate to your friend everything that comes to your mind. Don't forget, the first thought is always the best!

You may want to add some tools to your screen, such as a measure for the height, scales for the weight, and others. Take a good look at the color of the skin, the hair and the eyes, and every little detail you are able to catch.

After making the picture, proceed with the treatment in the regular way.

You and your friend are going to be astonished by the results! I have known some people who were not sure they have reached the alpha state at all, and their accuracy was over 80 percent in describing the subject! If that is the case with you, you are definitely ready for long-distance healing!

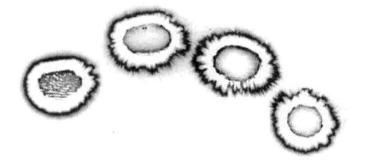

COMPLEMENTARY ENERGY TREATMENTS

Sometimes biotherapy itself is not enough to provide a total recovery, and there is a need to motivate the subject in order to speed up the healing process. In these cases we have to employ other types of treatments. Most of the modalities used to complement biotherapy are seemingly of a physical nature, however they all effect the energy systems of the body as well. The origins of these therapeutic methods also stretch back centuries throughout history, most of them being created in the Far East.

The most effective supplementary treatments can be classified into two major groups:
- Massage Therapy
- Pressure Point Therapy (Acupressure and Reflexology)
In addition, acupuncture is also recommended, however, it requires the knowledge and license of an acupuncture physician. Therefore, we are not going to discuss that option.

MASSAGE THERAPY

Massage is the systematic and scientific manipulation of the soft tissues of the body.

Massage can be traced back 5000 years and has gained popularity throughout history as an excellent therapeutic method that promotes the circulation of blood and lymph systems, relaxes muscles, relieves pain, improves balance, and boosts the overall energy of the body. Lately, it has been recognized as a superb restorer of the body's metabolic balance as well as a stress reliever.

There are countless varieties of massage therapy: Swedish, Chinese, French, English, German, Japanese, etc. Besides this classification, there are numerous methods categorized by their specific manipulation techniques: Neuromuscular Therapy, Trigger Point Therapy, Sports Massage, Polarity Therapy, Trager Therapy, Rolfing, and yes, Reflexology and Pressure Point Treatments. New systems emerge every day, thus it is impossible to name them all. There is also a wide range of mechanical devices available for soft tissue manipulation.

The benefits of massage are immeasurable, however it is important to mention how it can aid a biotherapy treatment.

Many times the imbalances in the energy field of the body are caused by the imbalances in the musculo-skeletal system. Bad posture, too much stress, muscular or arthritic pain, injuries, etc., all contribute to energy instability. When the body's energy balance is restored through biotherapy in these cases, the results are not long-lasting. The source of the problem is still not terminated. That is when we have to do some additional hands-on work. A good example of this fact is headaches. As much as 75% of all the headaches are tension related. We can stop them through biotherapy in matter of minutes, however, if the muscles of the neck are still tight, there is a good chance for those headaches to reoccur in the future. Relaxing the neck muscles with massage will greatly reduce the risk of tension-type headaches.

Therapeutic massage is strictly regulated by some states, and licensing is necessary for operation[1]. However, in some cases

---

[1]As of this moment, only 19 of the fifty states have regulations regarding therapeutic massage.

especially if you work on someone close to you for no profit whatsoever, you are allowed to give a good rubdown.

Therapeutic massage is so complex that it would require an entire book to teach, so I will try to give an insight only to the basic techniques that may be useful in your future work. The knowledge of anatomy and physiology is, however required. You have to know the muscles you massage.

In the following are described the major massage movements necessary for a basic massage.

Massage Movements

The most popular massage technique is indeed Swedish massage, brought to the west by Per Henrik Ling of Sweden (1776-1839). It provides the fundamentals for the majority of the massage techniques used today.

The movements are classified into five or more major groups, depending on various authors.

Effleurage (Gliding), the most common massage movement, is applied by gliding the hand over a portion of the body. It is routinely used as the beginning and the end of each massage session and also as the beginning and the end of massaging each body part. It can be superficial or deep. Superficial strokes apply very light touch and are used mostly for the above described procedure. Deep effleurage has a more mechanical effect, stretching and broadening the muscle tissue and fascia. If directed from the tendon towards the muscle belly, it also tends to stretch the tendon and relax the

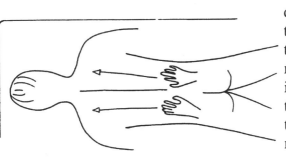

muscle. Gliding strokes generally follow the direction of the muscle fibers.

To apply effleurage, gently glide your hands over the skin or clothing without friction. Use your body weight to employ pressure, not only your arm strength. If you use lotion, the movement is much smoother! When the end of the portion of the body being massaged is reached, repeat the movement from the starting position. This movement itself, if done softly, can be performed for a longer period of time if only a calming effect is desired.

A general rule applies for gliding as for all the other massage movements: When massaging the extremities, the movements must always be directed from the end of the limb towards the center of the body, following the venous flow!!!

Petrissage (Kneading) is a movement that gently raises the skin and muscular tissue from their regular position. The muscles are then pinched, rolled, or squeezed between the thumb and the rest of the fingers. It is used mostly on fleshy areas of the body, usually in a circular motion. If performed on the limbs, it follows the venous flow. The "milking" motion also enhances the flow of the blood and lymph, helps break down the adhesions, and stretches the muscles.

To apply petrissage, gently squeeze the skin and muscle between your thumb and the rest of the fingers, making sure the skin touches your palm, and lift them up slightly pushing forward. Try not to pinch the skin. When you reach the highest position, relax the grip and repeat the movement. You may use both hands alternately. This movement, like all the others may be applied both on the bare skin or through clothes.

Friction. While kneading involves lifting of the muscle tissues, friction presses the superficial tissues against the deeper layers in order to flatten, stretch or broaden the muscles. As friction produces more heat, it also tends to speed up the metabolic rate. This movement helps to break down adhesions and separate the tissues, and also promotes absorption of fluid around the joints. The increased rubbing rushes blood to the superficial blood vessels making the skin red, although the skin itself is not the subject of the treatment.

Friction is performed by using the fleshy parts of either the palm, thumb or fingertips. The movements may be circular or directional.

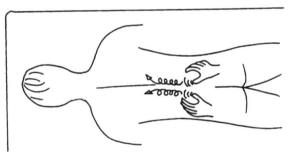

Circular friction is done by compressing the skin against the deeper layers of muscle and fascia in a continuously circular motion. After a few strokes, the pressure is released and you may repeat the procedure adjacent to the previous spot.

Directional movements may be cross-fiber or longitudinal. Cross-fiber friction is applied in a transverse direction, across the muscles.

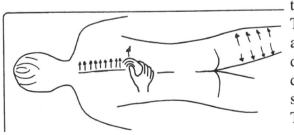

The strokes are short and deep, usually covering a small area. T h i s

movement encourages the formation of elastic fibrous tissue and stretches the muscles, tendons and ligaments.
Longitudinal friction follows the direction of the muscle fibers.

Friction may also be performed by simply compressing the muscle tissues with the palm of the hand. It is a very common move in sports massage and in massage through the clothes.

There are numerous other friction techniques, however, for our purposes these are enough to know.

Tapotement is less therapeutic than the other massage movements, usually performed when stimulation is desired.

It is executed by light, rhythmical beating of the skin by

the palm, blade of the hand, fist, fingertips, palm, etc. Let the hands relax with the fingers loose before starting tapotement. Do not hit hard!

Note: It is absolutely prohibited to use tapotement over the heart and the kidneys and of course, the head!

Vibration is a light tremulous movement created by the fingers or the hand causing the treated body part to vibrate. It has a wonderful soothing effect, following the path of the nerve.

The gentle, rhythmical movements are created by the whole forearm, keeping the wrist and fingers stiff, just like shaking dice. Keep the palm of your hand or the fingertips lightly touching the body.

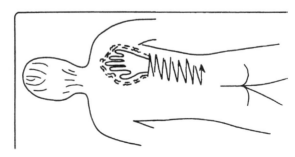

Vibration and tapotement may be performed by any of the numerous, popular massage devices, however, as we know, nothing can substitute for the human touch.

Application of Massage

Massage should be performed in a quiet, pleasant environment, with no hurry whatsoever. The movements have to be slow and relaxing, with the operator constantly touching the body of the subject until the end of the treatment. Massage can be executed anywhere and anytime, however, a proper massage table or chair, or a comfortable cushion will always enhance the enjoyment. If the use of lubrication is desired, chose a simple, non-allergenic lotion, preferably with no lanolin or mineral oils. The use of baby powder is also helpful. If the subject is unclothed, make sure to be professional, concealing the client's personal parts at all times! Regardless, with massage knowledge obtained solely from this book, you should consider massaging only through clothes!   For additional professional experience in the field of therapeutic massage, contact a board-approved massage school.

As an addition to massage, I can also recommend active and passive stretching and a lot of exercise.

Massage For Headaches

Whether a biotherapy session for headache relief was successful or not, a simple 5-10 minute massage will certainly ensure a positive outcome. In addition, sometimes a good rubdown is enough to alleviate the pain, without any energy work.

This massage technique is very simple and is done through clothing.

Have your subject in a seated position, chest against the back of the chair, leaning over a tabletop with the arms and the head resting on a comfortable pillow.

Start the massage by compressing the back with the palms of your hands on both sides of the spine. Go from the top towards the low back, using your weight instead of your arm strength. The best way is to keep your feet in a bow stance described in a previous chapter, which will give you the greatest control over your own posture.

Repeat the movement the opposite direction, this time increasing the pressure. You may follow the downward route once again, using only your thumbs, compressing the laminar groove, which is the fleshy area close to the spine. Compress for a couple of seconds and then move on approximately 1-2 inches. You can also repeat this movement upwards.

When the top of the back is reached, start kneading the upper trapezius on both sides simultaneously (the top of the shoulders on each side of the neck) for a couple of minutes. This is one of the most popular massaging areas!

From this section move up slowly to the neck area and knead it with only one hand, first lightly, then if no discomfort is detected, increase the pressure. You may also do circular

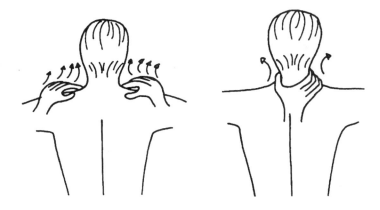

friction with your fingertips on both sides of the cervical spine. Try not to go past the midline of the neck which hosts some major blood vessels (carotid arteries and jugular veins)! After a few minutes move up to the occipital area, which is the base of the skull. Decrease the pressure and continue with light circular friction. Your movements should always be slow, even and relaxed.

Extend your massage to the skull, too. Using all the fingertips, perform small compressions on the head, as if you were washing the hair. Cover the whole hair area, slowly moving around. When the front is reached, massage the temples - the soft area located beside the eyes - with light circular movements.

Slowly come back the same way, lightly touching the head, down the neck and to the upper trapezius. You may finish by a

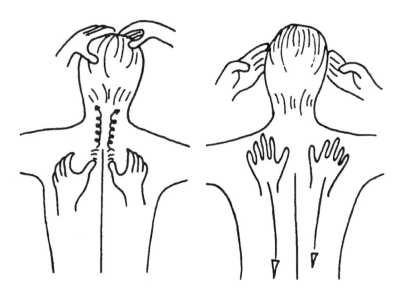

few more strokes of kneading on that area and softly brushing off the back.

For best results, you can always customize your massage to soothe your subject's desires. If no conversation is going on, just use your own perception and experience.

The length of this massage is completely up to you, however, 15 minutes is enough to serve the purpose.

Back Rub

A simple back massage can also be performed in the same seated position.

Start the same way - compressing the back from top to the bottom continuing with the thumb compressions. In addition, you may perform circular friction on the muscles on both sides of the spine. Be careful! Don't press on the vertebrae!

Cross fiber friction is a good continuation after the circular movements. The depth of the pressure depends entirely on the tolerance of your subject.

As an addition, kneading can be performed on the latissimus dorsi- the wide muscles of the back, in a lengthwise fashion.

You may repeat every movement as many times as you wish, again, depending on your subject.

The end of the back rub can be the same as with the previous massage, except you may do some tapotement on the upper back before you finish.

The two massages described above can freely be combined into one session. They are easy to execute, and of course, with practice and experience they will become an invaluable part of your therapies.

PRESSURE POINT THERAPY

Pressure point therapy simply refers to finger compression to certain points of the body for therapeutic purposes. Many known methods in this field include Acupressure, Jin Shin Do, Shiatsu, and Reflexology. The first three are based on the theory and practice of acupuncture, and its meridians and acupuncture points, while reflexology is based on the theory of reflex points.

Again, because of the extreme multitude and availability of the material, I will mention only the parts that are of importance to us. This includes basic acupressure and reflexology.

ACUPRESSURE

Acupressure simply refers to treatment by finger pressure to acupuncture points. The main aspects of acupuncture have been discussed earlier. Because of the excessive length of the subject, I will limit the presentation to only a few major points that are of special interest to our practice, namely headaches and back pain. These two distresses require more attention as reoccurring problems in modern society. While they may successfully be treated with biotherapy, most of them are of chronic nature, demanding additional means of treatment. Acupressure can be one of them.

Application of Acupressure

Acupressure is applied by the thumb or the middle finger to the acupuncture point. The depth of the pressure depends on the tolerance of the recipient and the nature of the problem. For chronic complications the pressure should be as deep as possible. Precision is very important! The exact point must be found. A way to do it, if you know the location, is to start with light compression, circling the fingertip over the acu-point. As you increase the pressure, decrease the diameter of the circles. The ultimate objective is a deep, constant pressure to the acupuncture point. The time of the treatment ranges from one to five minutes per point, or until relief is achieved.

As a beginner, make sure not to use this technique over areas that shouldn't be massaged either, namely: scar tissues, contusions, infections, or any other sensitive regions.

Acupressure For Headaches

These points are usually massaged until the headache is stopped, however, sometimes it is hard to determine precisely which point is the correspondent one, in which case you need to work on all of them.

To locate the acu-points below, you need some knowledge of anatomy, although it is easy to find them on the corresponding charts.

Acupressure points for headache relief:

1) Gall Bladder-20 (GB-20). Excellent for both tension and migraine headaches. Located on the back of the head, at the tip of the mastoid process, in the groove formed between the sternocleidomastoid and the trapezius muscles.

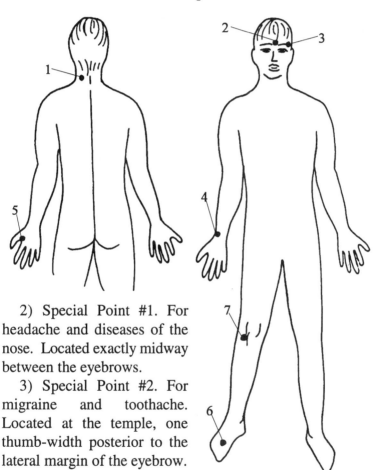

2) Special Point #1. For headache and diseases of the nose. Located exactly midway between the eyebrows.

3) Special Point #2. For migraine and toothache. Located at the temple, one thumb-width posterior to the lateral margin of the eyebrow.

4) Lung-7 (Lu-7). For headaches, neck pain, asthma and cough. Located proximally to the styloid process of the radius.

5) Large Intestines-4 (LI-4). A universal and very popular point for foreheadache, toothache, fever, asthma, anesthesia for

dental work, etc. Located between the first and second metacarpals, in the corner formed by the open thumb and forefinger. Very painful when pressed!

6) Liver-3 (Li-3). For headache. Located between the first and second metatarsals, distal to the heads.

7) Stomach-36 (St-36). For headache, foreheadache, fever, shock, epilepsy, etc. Located one thumb-width distal and lateral to the tibial tuberosity.

Acupressure For Back Pain

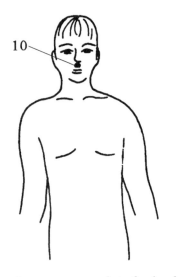

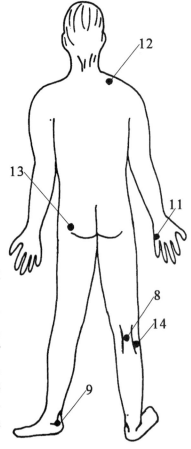

Acupressure points for back pain relief:

8) Urinary Bladder-40 (B-40). For low back pain, sciatica, leg cramps, lower extremity paralysis, arthritis, epilepsy, etc. Located at the center of the popliteal fossa - on the midline behind the flexed knee.

9) Urinary Bladder-60 (B-60). For low back pain, sciatica, lower extremity paralysis. Located on the middle between the Achilles tendon and the lateral malleolus.

10) Governing Vessel-26 (GV-26). For low back pain, epilepsy, shock... Located one third of the distance from the inferior nose to the upper lip line.

11) Small Intestine-3 (SI-3). For low back pain, neck pain, occipital (back of the head) headache. Located at the apex of the distal palmar crease on the ulnar side of the clenched fist.

12) Gall Bladder-21 (GB-21). For shoulder, neck, and back pain. Located halfway between C-7 and acromion process.

13) Gall Bladder-30 (GB-30). For sciatica, low back pain, hip joint pain... Located at one third of the distance from the greater trochanter to the base of the coccyx.

14) Gall Bladder-34 (GB-34). For low back, lower extremity, and knee pain. Located anterior to the neck of the fibula.

In addition you may also use #1 and #4 to relieve neck pain.

REFLEXOLOGY

Reflexology or Zone Therapy is based on a concept similar to the theory of Iridology (Iris diagnoses) and Ear-Acupuncture (Auricular points), meaning that certain areas of the body are connected to some other distant organs or tissues, thus "reflecting" the situation in those body parts. Through this knowledge, a therapist may stimulate the body's own healing process by compressing and massaging specific areas located on the feet or the hands. Contrary to the general belief, reflex points are also located on other parts of the body, besides the above mentioned. For instance, the knees are connected to the elbows, the hips to the shoulders, and so on.

As many other healing arts, this too originated in China. It was brought to the United States in 1913 by William H. Fitzgerald.

How reflexology really works is still a mystery. However, to prove the connection between distant body parts is easy. Just rub the middle toe on your foot for a few minutes (which is the reflex point of your middle finger), and you'll notice the middle finger of your hand getting slightly warmer, caused by the elevated blood flow to the area.

The charts for reflexology are easy to follow and are self explanatory. You don't need long hours to study, especially if you start with the reflex points on the feet. Just imagine the feet as a mirror of a whole person. The easiest way is to start with the inside of the foot, from top to the bottom. The big toe is the head, while the "moving" part on it is the neck, followed by the part resembling the spine. Everything else is built around it! At the exact middle of the foot is the location of the kidney!

When doing reflexology the major rule to follow is: Everything over the neck is reflected on the opposite foot, thus the right eye's reflex point, for instance, is located on the left foot. On the contrary, everything below the neck is reflected on the foot that is on the same side. For instance, the left kidney's reflex point is right in the middle of the left foot.

The "feeling" for reflexology comes with experience, however if you seriously think about practicing it, you should consider a good teacher for the final tips.

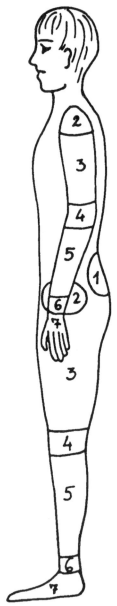

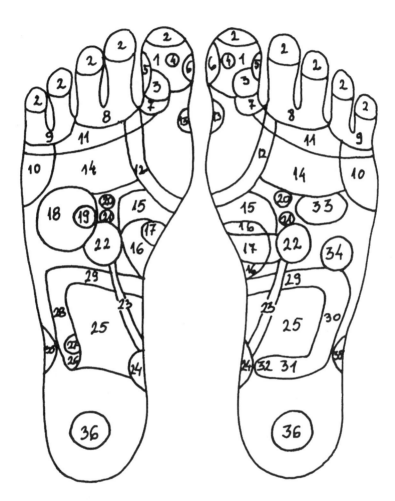

REFLEX POINTS OF THE FEET
1 HEAD/BRAIN (CEREBRUM)
2 SINUSES
3 CEREBELLUM
4 HYPOPHYSIS
5 TEMPLE (TRIGEMINAL NERVE)
6 NOSE
7 NAPE
8 EYE
9 EAR
10 SHOULDER
11 TRAPEZIUS
12 THYROID GLAND
13 PARATHYROID GLAND
14 LUNG, BRONCHUS

15 STOMACH
16 DUODENUM
17 PANCREAS
18 LIVER
19 GALL BLADDER
20 SOLAR PLEXUS
21 ADRENAL GLAND
22 KIDNEY
23 URETER
24 BLADDER
25 SMALL INTESTINES
26 APPENDIX

27 ILEOCECAL VALVE
28 ASCENDING COLON
29 TRANSVERSE COLON
30 DESCENDING COLON
31 SIGMOID COLON
32 RECTUM, ANUS
33 HEART
34 SPLEEN
35 KNEE
36 GONADS (TESTES OR OVARIES)

Reflex Points of the Outside of the Feet

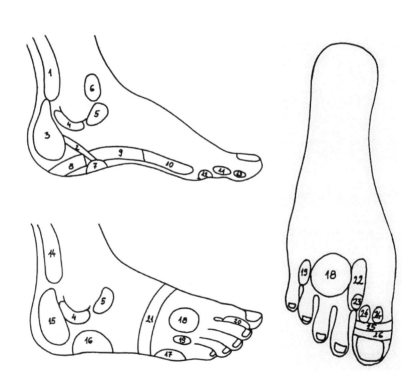

REFLEX POINTS OF THE OUTSIDE OF THE FEET
1 RECTUM
2 URETHRA, PENIS OR VAGINA
3 PROSTATE OR UTERUS
4 HIP JOINT
5 LYMPH NODES
6 GROIN
7 BLADDER
8 TAILBONE
9 LOW BACK - LUMBAR VERTEBRAE
10 UPPER BACK - THORACIC VERTEBRAE
11 NECK - CERVICAL VERTEBRAE
12 PARATHYROID GLAND
13 NOSE
14 RELAXATION ZONE FOR MENSTRUAL CRAMPS
15 GONADS (TESTES OR OVARIES)
16 KNEE
17 SHOULDER
18 CHEST
19 CENTER FOR EQUILIBRIUM
20 TEMPLE (TRIGEMINAL NERVE)
21 DIAPHRAGM
22 LYMPH VESSELS
23 LARYNX, TRACHEA
24 TONSILS
25 LOWER JAW
26 UPPER JAW

REFLEX POINTS OF THE HAND

1 SINUSES
2 BRAIN
3 HEAD
4 THROAT
5 NECK
6 TAILBONE
7 LOW BACK - LUMBAR VERTEBRAE
8 UPPER BACK - THORACIC VERTEBRAE
9 EAR
10 EYE
11 LUNG
12 SHOULDER
13 SOLAR PLEXUS
14 KIDNEY
15 ADRENAL GLAND
16 PANCREAS
17 LIVER
18 GALL BLADDER
19 STOMACH
20 THYROID GLAND
21 APPENDIX
22 ASCENDING COLON
23 TRANSVERSE COLON
24 SMALL INTESTINES
25 BLADDER
26 HIP/KNEE
27 TESTES/OVARIES
28 PENIS OR UTERUS/ PROSTATE

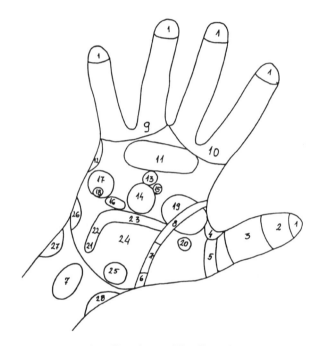

Application of Reflexology

The foot or hand massage consists of light to deep compressions to the reflex points, executed by the thumbs of the therapist. As all the dysfunctions of the body are reflected on those areas, with a little practice, it is easy to detect them, just by pressing the corresponding points. For example, if there is a problem with the left ear, its reflex point on the right foot will be tender when compressed. Thus, a whole body diagnosis may be done by systematically covering the whole foot with thumb pressure. Anywhere a discomfort is located is an area that needs attention. If your subject has no specific complaints, this is the way to go.

When the "unhealthy" zones are located, proceed with the treatment: Massage those sites with your thumb in a small, circular fashion. This way every circle will definitely "hit the spot". The length of rubbing varies, however a whole reflexology session usually doesn't exceed thirty minutes. Every point may be massaged for up to five minutes (in some cases even ten or fifteen), except the areas of the liver and the spine, which require special care. The zone of the liver may be massaged over five minutes only in the case of the kidneys being in perfect condition, otherwise too much poisonous material will get into the blood stream, making it impossible to discharge. The spine's zones should not be massaged too long because of possible reactions caused by elevated blood flow to the area.

The reflexology session should follow the general rules of massage. Make sure your subject is positioned comfortably, seated or lying down. The environment should be clean and cozy. You should also be seated in a relaxed position, with the feet of your client placed in front of you or on your lap.

In some cases, you will need to immerse the feet in hot water for ten or fifteen minutes before the session to soften the hard calluses.

The advantage of reflexology over acupressure is that the zones are located in a small accessible area, making it possible for anyone to treat themselves. When I was overwhelmed with clients in my biotherapy practice, I didn't have any time to use other modalities. To counter that, I would keep copies of the foot-reflexology chart, and for each person I would mark the zones to be massaged, thus making them able to help themselves. The results were outstanding! The notion that they can actually aid their own recovery sped up the healing process tremendously. And, if there were no positive results, I would just ask: Well, did you do your homework? In most cases the answer was negative. As you see, this is a perfect way to treat laziness. People should realize that their best doctor is in their head. Your job is to tell them how to reach that doctor.

Reflexology For Headaches

As we know by now, biotherapy is the fastest way to relieve headaches. Neck massage and reflexology are the necessary additions to the treatment for lasting results. Massage will release the tightness in muscles, while the reflex zone treatment will actually increase the blood and energy flow to the treated area, in its mysterious ways, providing a long-term healing effect. In addition, reflexology may be performed by the subject himself as part of a self-treatment program. To relieve an acute headache, reflexology is not even nearly as effective as the other methods discussed. Nevertheless, it works excellently in handling chronic headaches. In some cases though (for instance menstrual cramps), rubbing the corresponding zones will indeed almost instantly stop the pain.

To treat headaches, reflexology practitioners simply suggest massaging the reflex areas of the head, and possibly changing the diet. This second part of the treatment is more difficult and depends mainly upon the headache sufferer. Many times headaches are caused by certain foods, which can be the case especially with migraine headaches. A study conducted in England in the 1970's came up with the foods most frequently (and most likely) causing migraines. These are: Wheat, oranges, eggs, tea, coffee, chocolate, milk, beef, corn, cane sugar, yeast, mushrooms, and peas. Surprised?! Most of us regularly consume at least one of these, but it doesn't mean we'll get a headache from it. However, if headache sufferers record their eating habits, they may come up with a certain food, or food group that is the cause of their problem. Until then keep on working on them.

As we see, reflexology is very simple and self-explanatory. Just follow the charts and your own senses, and let time and the body's own healing powers do the rest.

CASE STUDIES

The following case studies are selected from my personal files in order to give you an insight to biotherapy treatments. A universal rule can not be derived from them, because of the vast differences between each individual, however, I truly hope that my experience will help you in your future work. Some of the examples reflect the exact treatment, while some are generalized for easier understanding.

Headaches

Headache is probably the most common ailment treated by a biotherapist. The extremely high number of headache sufferers has so far had to rely solely on pain medication, which suppresses the symptoms, but doesn't treat the problem itself. The variety of causes ranges from stress, diet, injury, bad posture, to harmful electromagnetic radiation, and many more, making it most difficult
to find the solution. In some cases, chiropractic adjustment, massage therapy, or acupuncture can provide relief, however they are effective in only a fraction of all cases.

In general, headache treatments by biotherapy look the same: Evaluation, or assessment of the energy field, followed by taking off the excess energy (which usually ends the pain) and then balancing the energy field. The treatments should be conducted in either a sitting or standing position. The imbalances in the aura range from areas around the head (always) to the neck and stomach regions. The signals you may get at the forehead always require feedback from your subject to accurately evaluate. Imbalances at the third eye usually indicate headaches, although they can also mean problem of the sinuses or eyes, or even low blood pressure!

The most common movement for relieving a headache is definitely the sweeping motion, however, the pulling and the circular movements are also used in certain situations. A little trick can also be helpful: If you lay your hands on the painful areas of the head for 10-20 seconds before taking off any energy, some of your own energy will enter your subjects field, thus making it easier to manipulate! Just be careful. This surplus may result in more pain if not taken off right away.

The number of sessions depends on the type, the frequency, and the eventual reoccurrence of the headaches. Sometimes other manual treatments are needed, including reflexology, which can be done by the subjects themselves.

The rate of success in treating headaches by biotherapy is believed to be over 90%, although I know hardly anyone that I couldn't affect!

Examples:

B.R. (35) has had headaches, problem with balance, dizziness, loss of hearing, and has been unable to sleep well.

Assessment: General imbalances in the energy field around the head, with no specific area.

Treatments were conducted for five days in a row, including assessments, taking off the excess energy around the head, and balancing the aura. B.R. was in sitting position during the treatments, because of the dizziness.

B.R. felt better after each session, however, the next day all the symptoms reoccurred. There was no improvement after five days. Then, he mentioned that he had been sleeping in the same spot for five years, which is exactly the length of the time he has had these problems. After measuring the energy fields in his bedroom by dowsing, I found a strong negative area right under the headboard of his bed. Once he moved the bed to the other end of the room, we repeated the five-day treatment. This time the results were outstanding. The headaches and the sleeping disorder totally vanished. He still had trouble with balance, although it also has improved. The sessions were repeated once more two weeks later, this time (considering there were no headaches) giving more energy to the center for balance, resulting in even better equilibrium and improved hearing.

P.P. (10) has had bad headaches of the forehead and the temples. Parents had tried everything from medication to acupuncture, but nothing helped. The everyday pain had affected the results in school and pushed this otherwise very intelligent and cheerful boy to depression.

Assessment: Excess energy at the forehead and the neck area.

Treatments were conducted for five days in a row, including assessment of the aura, taking off the excess energy and balancing the energy field. All in standing position.

P.P. felt the energy right away. He sensed heat and tingling, and especially the coolness when the energy was taken off. With that, his headache disappeared. There was no apparent headache for two weeks, except one occasion. The treatments were then repeated one more time, giving a lasting result.

M.M. (45) has had headaches, pain of the wrist joints and the neck, and nervousness. The distress increased during changes in weather.

Assessment: Besides having bad posture, M.M. had several imbalances in the aura, especially in the neck area. It seemed as if the neck chakra was totally disfigured. That was probably the reason for all the problems, however there were also imbalances in the wrists.

Treatments were conducted for five days, in standing position. After the assessment, I would start sweeping off the energy around the head, with the emphasis on the neck area.

The movements would continue down the spine and be repeated down the arms. After the pain had ceased, I would balance the aura and finish the session by closing it.

M.M. was very satisfied with the treatment. All her problems disappeared, including the discomfort during weather changes. We never had to repeat the therapy.

K.M. (31) Had tension headaches which she attributed to her stressful lifestyle.

Assessment: A strong abundance of energy was detected at the neck area, with a slight imbalance on the left side of the head. K.M.'s neck muscles were very tense and sensitive to pressure.

Treatments: As she was a busy person, sessions were conducted only once a week. After opening the aura, I took off the excess energy around the head, which gave her instant relief. There were no other imbalances, so I just equalized the energy field and finished the biotherapy part of the session. In addition, while she was in sitting position, I gave her a fifteen minute massage on her neck and adjacent muscles, which relaxed her even more. I also gave her neck stretches and suggested self treatment through reflexology.

The first couple weeks, K.M. experienced soreness in the neck from the massage treatments, but her headaches slowly diminished. After eight sessions (eight weeks), the headaches totally stopped.

Treating headaches is always full of surprises. Some have to be fought by every means, while some go away as if they never existed. That is what happened to Mr. P., who had suffered terrible migraines for over twenty years. His brother knew me, so at a party that we all attended, he suggested a biotherapy session. Although very skeptical, Mr. P. agreed to try me out right on the spot. His headache vanished after five minutes. Surprised that he never called for another session, I forgot about this incident, until, five years later, when we met on the street. "So, why didn't you call me?" I asked. The reply blew my mind. "What for? I haven't had a headache since!"

Back and Neck

Problems of the back are so complex that only a small percentage can be successfully treated by biotherapy. Easing the pain is always possible, however, if the distress is of a physical nature, biotherapy has to be supplemented by other therapeutic methods. If none of the previously mentioned modalities help, leave it to professionals such as chiropractors, osteopaths, medical doctors, massage therapists, or physical therapists.

The back is very sensitive to all the imbalances in the system. Our bodies constantly fight gravity, therefore, if we have poor posture, the first body part to suffer is the back. Most affected is the low back and the neck, which have no solid support, contrary to the thoracic vertebrae which are supported by the ribs. A shorter leg, dislocated hip, weak back muscles, etc., and even a wallet in the back pocket can all cause your back to "go out of balance". This notion requires you to use more caution when assessing the back.

The imbalances of the energy field around the spine are usually connected to the chakras or to specific injuries of the spine. The most common areas are the neck, mid-thoracic region and lumbar area, however, they don't always signal the problems of the spine or the surrounding muscles. Therefore, you regularly have to ask your subject for feedback.

Common confusions:
-Signal at the neck can mean:
-neck pain (of muscular or other origins)
-headaches
-high blood pressure
-shoulder problems

-Signal at the mid-thoracic area of the back can mean:
-pain
-asthma, bronchitis, smoker's lungs, or any other lung problem, even if it occurred a long time ago
-problems of the heart
    -Signal at the lumbar area can mean:
-pain
-any distress of the adjacent internal organs
-leg pain
    When the zones with surplus energy are found, proceed to take off energy by any of the movements. Before closing the aura you may secure a longer lasting effect by moving your hand up and down by the spine, thus assisting the energy flow.
    In the following, I will show some extreme cases that were treated by biotherapy without requiring other manual treatments.
    L.T. (25) had a constant neck and shoulder pain for several months.
    Assessment showed an imbalance at the neck, slightly turned towards the left shoulder.
    Treatments were conducted for five days, the usual way, in a sitting position. The aura stabilized quickly and easily, however the pain reoccurred a week later.
    At the second attempt to treat the problem, I suggested that she try reflexology. During the initial foot massage, I discovered a corn on the medial side of the large toe on the left foot. This was placing a constant pressure on the reflex zones of the neck and shoulder.
    When the corn was surgically removed at my suggestion, the energy equilibrium remained steady after only one additional session, and the discomfort dissipated.
    T.G. (41) had been suffering from chronic low-back pain for many years. He had tried different manual treatments, however, only pain medication could give him even temporary relief.

Assessment showed a strong surplus of energy at the lumbar area, in spite of the muscles being remarkably soft. This led to the conclusion that the problem was solely of energy nature.

Treatments. After the initial energy balancing treatment, I measured the negative energy in T.G.'s bedroom, which showed a strong negative force under the middle of his bed. He had slept there for only a year, but there is a possibility that the previous location was also negative.

After moving the bed to a safe area, we completed a two week therapy of ten sessions. After that, there was no soreness left.

Asthma and Bronchitis

The two most common respiratory ailments of children, as well as adults, are exceptionally easy to treat by biotherapy. Some of the improvements are registered as soon as the first session is completed! The results vary slightly depending on the age of the subject (the younger, the better).

The imbalances in the aura are very characteristic and are similar in both cases. The particular areas are the back of the neck, the front and back heart chakras (middle of the thorax on both front and back), and sometimes the area above the heart. Imbalances are randomly recorded around the solar plexus chakras, too.

Examples:
C.J. (12) - asthma with frequent attacks.
G.T. (11) - asthma.
A.T. (3) - asthma.
V.T. (4) - chronic bronchitis.
S.D. (1,5)- chronic bronchitis.
S.M. (58) - asthma, headaches, low blood pressure.
B.K. (78) - asthma, abdominal pain.
T.V. (66) - asthma with frequent attacks, low back pain.

S.K. (70) - chronic bronchitis, abdominal pain, weak legs.

G.K. (50) - asthma, low back pain, nervousness.

Besides treating the additional problems, all of these people were handled in the same way as far as respiratory ailments are concerned. After spreading the aura, the assessment showed coinciding, typical areas of imbalances in all these cases. If no pain was detected in those areas, energy was added in order to balance the field. The pattern is usually the same: Giving energy to the neck, then to the lungs, and continuing with the rest. In some situations you need to subtract bioenergy from the lungs before filling it up, in order to make the process easier.

The sessions in all the above instances were conducted daily and ranged from one to two weeks. The cases are all from five years ago, which demonstrates the duration of the outcome. The results speak for themselves:

C.J. experienced improvement right away. The attacks became less frequent, finalizing at about one per week, instead of almost one per day.

G.T. had absolutely improved after only five sessions. No asthma attacks have been registered since.

A.T. felt perfect for five months. Then she started coughing and gasping for air again. The therapy was repeated once more, with an additional session two months later. Since then, she has been fine.

V.T. didn't cough for three weeks after the initial therapy, then the difficulties started again, although not with the same intensity. Another five sessions later, he was fine.

S.D. continued coughing, but less frequently and with less intensity. He never gasped for air again.

S.M.'s asthma and headaches totally disappeared after five sessions. Last time we spoke, three months later, she was still fine.

B.K. needed additional treatments, because of a strong negative area in her bedroom. After relocating the bed, the results were better. Only some occasional coughing remained.

T.V. got rid of her pain, however the asthma remained, although with much less frequent attacks.

S.K. has been breathing easier, and her energy level has been higher.

G.K. has had no back pain since, and even though asthma still remains, she has had fewer attacks.

Bed Wetting

The reason I have to mention this matter is that the common problem of "bed wetting" hasn't been adequately explained by modern medicine, yet. It has been treated by medications or by counselling, but with a very low rate of success.

As I became known, many people approached me to help treat their kids with my "miracle". I was hesitant at the beginning, since I knew nothing about the subject. One day, however, when I had enough "candidates", I decided to give it a try and maybe find a pattern for my future work.

I had six kids to work with for a whole week: N.J. (12), and his brother N.M. (7), M.G. (7.5), and his brother M.V. (4), A.D. (5.5), K.S. (8); and one adult, G.K. (43), who had needed to get up several times a night for the past few years.

At the initial assessment with all of them, I sensed a standard imbalance in their auras: The back of the neck, the solar plexus area both on the front and the back, stretching to the kidneys, and the bladder area. The latter two were no surprises, but the neck was something I didn't expect. Nonetheless, giving energy to those areas proved to be beneficial. The auras balanced out relatively easy, and the results were fabulous.

N.J. stopped bed wetting after the second session, while his brother stopped after the first one! M.G. stopped after four sessions, but it lasted only ten days. After an additional week of treatments, his problem didn't return for at least six months, which was the last time I heard of him. The only problem I had was with his little brother, who continued wetting in bed, although not so frequently. A.D. and K.S. had no additional treatments, their problem was history after only a week! The adult, G.K. wrote in my register: "Everything's super!" This tells it all.

This example should encourage you to experiment. If you have a chance to gather more people with the same (for you unknown) problem, go for it! You'll learn more from your own experience than from any book.

High/Low Blood Pressure

Hypertension (high blood pressure) is one of the main plagues of the twentieth century. Caused mainly by poor dietary habits, or by high stress level, or other reasons, it can be controlled by medication, however, a full improvement can be accomplished only by major changes in lifestyle. Any way we look at it, it requires a lot of devotion from an individual to get rid of it, that is, without the help of biotherapy. Studies and my personal experience reveal a high success rate in treating both high and low blood pressure. Of course, for a long lasting result, a change in lifestyle is indeed required, in spite of the fast effect accomplished by energy-balancing.

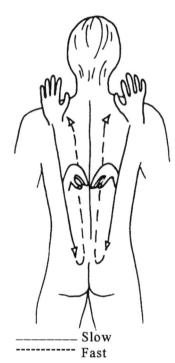

———— Slow
------------ Fast

There is nothing easier than to normalize high blood pressure by biotherapy. The whole procedure is standard, including assessment, energy transfer and closing the aura. The major area of imbalance in high blood pressure is the back of the neck, giving off a steady warm signal. The characteristic movement to lower the blood pressure is similar to mesmerizing, or relaxing the aura.

Start by holding your hands a few inches over the shoulders, then, with your palms slightly turned downwards and towards the body, pull the energy slowly down towards the coccyx (the base of the spine). Let your hands and wrists relax, then quickly go back to the shoulders and repeat the movements.
Continue for a few minutes. You subjects will usually feel more relaxed. Normally, between five and twenty sessions (depending on your bioenergetic capacity) provide a longer lasting relief.

Low blood pressure can be sensed on the forehead, between the eyebrows as a warm signal, just like hypertension on the neck.

Raising blood pressure is the exact opposite of the previous procedure. Start with your hands at coccyx level, wrists, hands and finger relaxed, with palms turned towards you. A few inches away from the back, slowly pull the energy up, towards the shoulders. When the end of that path is reached, quickly let your hands back to the starting position. Keep repeating the movements for a few minutes. The immediate outcome is amazing. Your subject will feel as if he has had a strong cup of coffee!

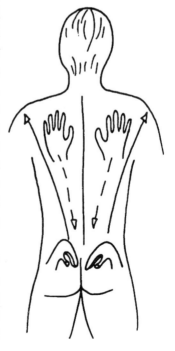

The success rate in my personal experience is over 80%, however when first meeting this problem, make sure a professional is following your

work. Only your subject's doctor is allowed to lower his
medication.

Problems of the Nose, Ears, and Eyes

As we have learned so far, virtually anything can be treated
by biotherapy. From the simplest headache to gangrene, we can
always expect some improvement, sometimes even miracles.

One of the fastest "miracles" is indeed opening a stuffy nose.
This procedure works almost every time and may be executed
in two different ways. The first one is the conventional energy
balancing session, which consists of assessment, taking off
excess energy around the nose, and closing the aura. Note that
we take off energy even though there is no pain involved. This
is an exception to the general rule. The second method of
"unstuffing" a runny nose is much faster. Stand on the right side
of your subject. Do a quick assessment of the energy only
around the nose and the front of the head, which will "disturb"
the energy field just enough to start your procedure. After that,
with your right hand, hold the person's nose up close to the eyes
with the thumb on one side and the fingertips of the last three
fingers on the other. The forefinger should rest on the middle
of the forehead at the same time. This positioning covers some
acupuncture points connected to the sinuses, thus speeding up
the whole process. Now, concentrate on giving energy for a
while. Your subject will feel the heat coming from your hand.
After a few minutes, loosen the grip and take off the excess
energy by sweeping movements, from the forehead towards the
chin and below. Your subject will immediately feel coolness
around the nose. The stuffiness will disappear within seconds!

All other sinus problems may be treated in similar manner.

Ear-ache is treated in the same fashion as any other pain,
except, because of the small area involved, you have to take off
energy by the "salting" movements. Hearing difficulties, and
noise in the ear, however, are more complex and require some

additional time, though they are relatively easy to treat with energy work. Problems with hearing, if they are treatable, demand at least 10 treatments to show minimal improvement. If there are no signs of healing after that time, unfortunately there is not much we can do.

Noise in the ear, however, is very much curable. I have stopped it many times before, with less than five treatments. The most interesting case happened only a year ago, involving a dear friend of my family. The lady had about 80% loss of hearing in her left ear, and a terrible noise, which had not ceased since it started two years before. Her radio was always blasting, even when she went to sleep, to suppress the noise. She had tried everything possible to get rid of this problem, but after numerous different therapies involving contemporary medicine, homeopathy in Europe, and even the famous Mayo clinic, there was no improvement. One day, when my wife found out about it, she suggested that she try biotherapy. The treatment was conducted in the classical fashion, except to concentrate more energy into the ear, I put my forefinger in it. According to her, the heat was very intense. The whole session lasted less then ten minutes, and the noise was gone! She just couldn't believe it! We repeated the session only once, a few days later. She didn't hear the noise for about six months, when it reoccurred, but with less intensity. We repeated the treatment, and since then she has been fine.

I have heard of many biotherapists claiming they can improve vision, or even enable people to get rid of their glasses. Unfortunately, I have no evidence to support those proclamations. I have worked on many people with eye problems before, but the only positive outcome I have achieved was that some of my clients have been able to see clearer. Improving vision, if possible at all, definitely requires a lot of bioenergy from the therapist. For some reason, I wasn't able to "throw away" anyone's glasses, however, this doesn't mean it's impossible. Keep on trying!

Diabetes

Healthy individuals have about 80 to 120 mg of glucose in every 100 ml of blood. Glucose is the smallest particle of sugar broken down by fermentation, and is the main energy source of the cells. After a generous meal the glucose level in blood rapidly rises. The pancreas immediately gets the signal and introduces insulin to the blood to normalize the blood sugar level. If the pancreas (actually the pancreatic islets) is not able to produce enough insulin, there will be an elevated blood glucose level, which, if surpassing the 160 mg% level, forces the kidneys to retain sugar from the blood, to protect the body from falling into coma. This condition is called type I diabetes mellitus. Type II diabetes is a result of abnormalities of the insulin receptors, which prevent the normal effect of insulin on its target cells, also raising blood sugar level. Type I is usually acquired by birth, while type II diabetes may affect individuals later on in their lives.

Contemporary medicine treats diabetes by either adding insulin to the body through pills or injections, or by medications that stimulate the production of insulin in the pancreas. Although exercise is known to help, there is no actual cure for this condition.

Biotherapy and reflexology (especially their combination) have shown excellent results in treating diabetes - in practice. Over 50% of cases have shown improvement in less then a month of therapy. That is with type II diabetes, although there have been good results achieved with type I diabetes, too.

In general, diabetes is accompanied by lack of bioenergy around the kidneys and the pancreas area (which is located between the kidneys), however, often there are other imbalances in the system, too. This problem may also be detected on the feet, resulting in discomfort when the zones of the pancreas, the stomach, and the kidneys are pressed. These are the exact areas to be massaged during reflexology sessions.

For the areas with lack of bioenergy, simply adding energy is needed. If/when the body is able to hold the balance in the energy field, there is a good chance for the normalization of the blood glucose level. Usually there is an instant improvement, however not a long lasting one. Patience is absolutely required to achieve full recovery. Some therapies may stretch for as long as months.

Examples:

A.J. (63) has had problems with her blood circulation, her heart, and had diabetes. Her blood sugar level has been 185 mg% for a long time.

Assessment. There were imbalances in the energy field behind the neck, and around the heart, the kidneys, the pancreas, and the stomach areas.

Treatments were conducted every day for five days, including assessment, adding energy and closing the aura. There was no need for taking off any energy.

A.J.'s blood glucose level dropped to 85.5 mg% immediately after the first session, and has never elevated again. Her mood and energy rose every day of the therapy and lasted a long time.

This example is unfortunately exceptional. In all the other cases much more time was necessary to achieve a positive outcome.

T.F. (46) has had diabetes with blood glucose level reaching 247 mg% when untreated.

Assessment showed the standard areas of less energy: the kidneys, the stomach, and the pancreas.

Treatments were also conducted the usual way.

After three days of therapy the glucose level dropped to 175 mg%. After a week it rose up to 200 mg% and stayed there. Since then, we repeated the treatments, but the blood sugar level never came below 160 mg%, although it also never rose over 198 mg%. In conclusion, T.F. has had to continue treatments through insulin injections.

As you see, results are unpredictable. Due to my lack of

experience in long term treatments (over three months) of diabetes, I can only suggest you to be patient and not to give up. Healing of this problem indeed requires time!

Tumors, Cancer

One of the leading causes of death in the world, cancer has been treated by medication, chemotherapy, or surgery, providing disputable results. The outcome depends mainly on the stage the disease has reached, and on the body part or system that is attacked. If cancer is in advanced phase, there is not much hope for recovery. The same is the case with tumors.

In practice, biotherapy has shown to be fairly effective in healing cancer, and very competent in fighting tumors.

Tumors are handled as separate energy systems within the body's energy. Keeping this in mind, we have to draw energy out of them to weaken and eventually destroy them. If it sounds too easy, that is because it actually is. Finding the tumor in the energy field is not a problem, considering it gives off a strong heat signal. The easiest way to attack it is by adding some energy to it, using either hands-on, or some other energy-giving method. When the signal weakens, that is the sign that you have given enough energy. Follow this right away by taking off energy from the same area. What happens here is that your energy has been mixed with the tumor's energy, which makes it more susceptible to your influence. After that it is much easier to take off its energy. This process has to be repeated as often as possible, at least once a day. The time needed to defeat a tumor depends on its size, your bioenergetic capacity, and of course, on your experience. I have seen tumors disappear in matter of weeks! The outcome also depends on the individual who has been treated. A positive change in diet with the emphasis on detoxification is desirable, while self-reflexology is also very helpful. In reflexology the significance is on massaging the zones of the organ that has the tumor, and the zones of the lymphatic system.

Fighting cancer also requires a change in diet and reflexology on the same zones. Energy work involves only giving energy, in order to strengthen the body. The results are unpredictable for the reasons listed above.

At the age 86, my great-grandmother was diagnosed with cancer, that had spread virtually all over her body. The prognosis was that she had only three months to live. As a beginner biotherapist, I decided to start working on her, since there was nothing to lose. I stopped by her house almost every day and spent about fifteen minutes each time on adding energy. She enjoyed the attention and the heat that overtook her body every time. Having difficulties understanding the process, she simply called it praying. The "praying" went on for months, and then less frequently for years. Instead of three months, my great-grandmother lived another four years. She died at the age of 90 after a short illness.

Stroke

Stroke, or cerebrovascular accident, is a result of a hemorrhage or cessation of blood flow through cerebral blood vessels, causing destruction of neurons of the motor area of the cerebrum. The victims of stroke lose the voluntary movement of the parts of the body on the side opposite to the side of the brain where the stroke occurred. If there is any chance to recovery, it is indeed time-consuming and requires a whole new re-education of the body parts involved. It can take anywhere from months to years for the victims to regain their normal voluntary movements.

Biotherapy is an entirely new approach in the treatment of stroke victims. Experience has shown that recovery time can be cut down to half by balancing the energy field of the body. Balancing the field of stroke victims consists almost solely of adding energy to the deficient areas. Sometimes in a matter of days there are already apparent improvements. The first signs are usually more energy and better sensitivity to touch.

All of the above examples have been chosen to give you an insight to biotherapy sessions. Your own work will depend a lot on your commitment, your approach, and of course your ability to radiate, and your experience. As you have seen, there is little that is impossible. Virtually anything that is alive may be treated by bioenergy. Even long distances between you and your patients are not an obstacle. I have successfully treated everything from migraines to tumors, and mental imbalances such as attention deficit disorders, etc., over distances of thousands of miles. So, don't give up. You might be some people's last chance.

COMBINED WORK BY SEVERAL HEALERS

Just recently, a young lady who attends my T'ai Chi course arrived at the class in very low spirits. We asked her what the problem was, and she replied that her goddaughter, born just days before, might not survive the complications following the delivery. The baby was very weak, and in addition needed surgery to correct an intestinal abnormality. Apparently, a part of her intestines remained outside the abdominal cavity. Shortly after the operation, another surgical intervention was necessary to correct the deformity of the cardiac sphincter (the upper valve of the stomach). As a result, the newborn had to be fed through a G-tube, in addition to all the other extra care she required for survival.

My student was very upset at not being able to help, so I decided to gather everyone at the end of the class and perform a combined long-distance healing session. As it was an advanced class, I didn't have to explain much about the energy work. Everybody was clear with their abilities and familiar with visualization and meditation. We all formed a circle with the young lady in the middle. I led the group through some relaxation and visualization, so our work would be synchronized. The lady in the middle had to concentrate on her goddaughter, while the rest of us enhanced her energy. We went through the whole process of long-distance healing. As we have felt before, the sensation in all of us was incredible. We all felt intense heat and relaxation, and our bodies were tingling all over. The session lasted only about ten minutes, thanks to already being relaxed from T'ai Chi. Next week we found out that the baby was out of crisis the day following our session! As an addition, my student sent her more energy long-distance, and later on up-close, which no doubt helped in removing the G-tube.

This is just an example of how strong a collective work can be. However, a trained group would be capable of performing "miracles" practically any time. All of the members performing the session have to be trained in long-distance healing, with one of them leading the treatment, telling the others step by step what to do. The whole procedure is no different from an individual long-distance healing.

After the above incident, we decided to perform a healing session after each class, not only long-distance, but also on the individuals who were present in the group. The subject would take the middle of the circle, while the rest of us would work on him or her from a few feet away. The intensity of the sensations was always there and the results have been outstanding.

A study on the subject a few years ago showed that the magnitude of success of biotherapy unevenly multiplies proportionately to the number of the biotherapists involved. This means that if one biotherapist is able to fill up an energy field to 100% in 15 minutes, three biotherapists, with the same ability to radiate, would realize the same result not in five minutes, but in much less time. Also, if one biotherapist is only able to fill up a field to 50%, combined work of more healers would achieve a 100% success. So, give it a try! If there is a possibility, form a group with other colleagues. Not only will you be able to amplify your energies, but you will learn a lot from each other's experiences.

LITERATURE

Zdenko Domancic: *The Unbelievable Abilities of Men* (in Croatian)

Drasko Acimovic: *With Bioenergy To Health - The Phenomenon of Zdenko Domancic* (in Serbo-Croatian)

Alexander Lowen M.D.: *Bioenergetics*

Barbara Ann Brennan: *Hands of Light*

Dolores Krieger Ph.D.,R.N.: *Accepting Your Power to Heal - The Personal Practice of Therapeutic Touch*

Carla Galli: *Do You Want to Be a Phenomenon?* (in Hungarian)

Deepak Chopra M.D.: *Ageless Body, Timeless Mind*

Dr.Simoncsics Peter: *Acupuncture, Life-Energy, Health* (in Hungarian)

Hans-Peter Waldrich: *Esoteric fur Einsteiger* (Hungarian translation)

Dusan Moraca: *Radiesthesia* (in Serbo-Croatian)

Zhou Yong, Eory Ajandok, Orosz Miklos: *Qi Gong - Chinese Health- Exercise* (in Hungarian)

Michio *Kushi:Your Face Never Lies* (Hungarian translation)

Branislav and Ljubisa Stojanovic: *Bioenergy, A World Without Illness* (in Serbo-Croatian)

Branislav Stojanovic: *Bioenergy, Cosmogenerator* (in Serbo-Croatian)

Dr. Swami Shankardevananda Saraswati, MB, BS: *Yogic Management of Asthma and Diabetes and The Practices of Yoga for the Digestive System* (Serbo-Croatian translation)

Nancy and Esmond Gardner: *Five Great Healers Speak Here*
Dr. Joseph Murphy: *The Power of Your Subconscious Mind*
        (Hungarian   translation)
Thorwald Dethlefsen and Rudiger Dahlke: *Krankheit als Weg*
        (Hungarian translation)
Sudhir Kakar: *Shamans, Mistics and Doctors*
Dr. Olah Andor: *Self control* (in Hungarian)
Swami Chinmayananda: *Meditation - The Gateway to Freedom*
Jose Silva: *Mindcontrol*
Uri Geller: *My Story*
Dr. Tarackozi Istvan: *Touchless Healing* (in Hungarian)
Dr. Jurij Volkov: *About Bioenergy* (in Hungarian)
Choa Kok Sui: *Pranic Healing*
Michele Curcio: *La Parapsichologie de A a Z* (Hungarian
        translation)
Dr. Motus Janos: *Reflexology* (in Hungarian)
Mark F. Beck: *Theory and Practice of Therapeutic Massage*
Frances M. Tappan: *Healing Massage Techniques*
Hiroshi Motoyama: *Theories of the Chakras: Bridge to Higher
        Consciousness*
Paul Crompton: *The Elements of Tai Chi*
Bruce Kumar Frantzis: *Opening the Energy Gates of Your Body*
Donath Tibor: *Anatomical Names A-Z* (in Hungarian)
Hulda Regehr Clark, Ph.D., N.D.: *The Cure For All Diseases*

Index

ABOUT THE AUTHOR

Csongor Daniel, born August 4th, 1965, has had a colorful life. Coming from a Hungarian family in Yugoslavia, he grew up speaking two languages, which he later increased by three more. As a champion marksman, and also being involved in swimming and martial arts, he had an early brush with meditation, concentration and the use of internal energy. His gift of healing, however, surfaced only at age 21, when he was already an engineering student. Healing as a hobby turned serious when he accidently realized that he could move people without touching them. This psychokinetic ability led him on a path that he still follows. On his road to knowledge, he has met or worked with many great European healers, while reading all the available books on energy-healing in Serbo-Croatian, Hungarian, and English, mastering biotherapy, reflexology, and various therapeutic massage techniques. As an established biotherapist, Daniel (as he is known here) has had over thirty patients a day, successfully treating almost anything from simple headaches to the most serious medical conditions!

Thanks to the turmoil in his native country (and to his beautiful wife from New Jersey), his vacation in the USA in 1991 turned into a permanent stay. Since then he has been working as a Licensed Massage Therapist, biotherapist, massage teacher and T'ai Chi instructor.

During ten years of practice, he realized that one doesn't need to be gifted in order to heal himself and others. This conception led to the creation of this book.

T'ai Chi for Everyone

This 71 minute long, professional quality instructional video is one of a kind. It was developed for the absolute beginner, providing detailed explanation on each of the 18 movements of T'ai Chi Chi Kung, with front and back views for convenience. T'ai Chi Chi Kung (Taiji Qigong) consists of stationary exercises that anyone can easily master. The movements are light and soft with the emphasis on breathing. Recommended to anyone from 3 to 103!

The tapes were produced by Tampa One Productions, and may be ordered for $19.95 + $2.95 S&H, from:

NRG Works
2733 Lawyer Terrace
North Port, FL 34286
(941) 423-8660

Notes

Notes